Dimensional Mo
with
Fused & Painted Glass Elements

Author, Designer & Fabrication
Leslie Perlis

Text Editor
Randy Wardell

Book Layout & Typography
Randy Wardell • Carole Wardell

Photography
Leslie Perlis

Fabrication Assistance
Tim Pratt, Eric Pratt

Author's Acknowledgements

I want to thank my family and friends for their support and appreciation of my work. I especially thank my parents David & Adrienne Perlis, who encouraged me to pursue my chosen career in the arts and for not getting on my case to acquire a 'backup' teaching credential. Also thanks for moving us to San Diego CA, a beautiful city full of inspiring views and a sunny atmosphere.

I'm fortunate to be active and involved with an amazing local art glass community where I've had the opportunity to work with other glass professionals, to grow together as artists and to promote our craft through exhibits, workshops and social events.

I dedicate this book to my son Eric Pratt, who inspires me by teaching me new things and presenting new opportunities that keep me feeling young and connected with all that's happening in today's world.

I want to thank Randy & Carole Wardell for believing in me and my work, for their confidence to produce this second volume featuring my art and also for supporting art glass concepts and techniques that push our wonderful medium to new levels.

I hope this book provides an inspiration for others to pursue their own art glass potential, just as I have benefited from the sharing and caring of glass artists before me.

Published by

Wardell
PUBLICATIONS INC

Join our Next Step Art Glass webblog on our website www.nextstepartglass.com
by email: info@wardellpublications.com or visit our Website: www.wardellpublications.com

Dimensional Mosaics
with
Fused & Painted Glass Elements

Cataloging in Publication Data

Perlis, Leslie, 1952-

Dimensional mosaics with fused & painted glass elements / author, designer & fabrication: Leslie Perlis; text editor: Randy Wardell; photography: Leslie Perlis; book layout & typography: Randy Wardell, Carole Wardell; fabrication assistance: Tim Pratt, Eric Pratt.

ISBN-13: 978-0-919985-60-5

ISBN-10: 0-919985-60-2

1. Mosaics--Technique. 2. Glass craft. 3. Glass fusing. I. Wardell, Randy A. (Randy Allan), 1954- II. Title.

TT298.P46 2009   748.5028'5   C2009-906212-7

Printed in Thailand by Phongwarin Printing Ltd.
Published simultaneously in Canada and USA
Email: info@wardellpublications.com
Website: www.wardellpublications.com
Booksite: www.nextstepartglass.com

Table Of Contents

Next Step Instruction

ProTips

Dimensional Mosaics Projects

Author Contact Information

Perlis Studio

955 Cornish Dr.

San Diego, CA 92107 USA

Phone: 619-222-8776

Email: info@leslieperlis.com

Website: www.leslieperlis.com

This is the hand of a dancer. Her bracelet of torch worked beads was made by Heather Trimlett. See the rest of this dancer, along with her friend on the dance floor on page 38.

Meet Stix the teenage rock star. He has his music, his drums and his sticks and is ready for his next gig. Turn to page 32 for more dish on this young performer.

Introduction

"My artistic philosophy is pretty straightforward; start with a clear and simple idea, add lots of art glass with vivid colors & textures plus a heavy dose of unrestricted creativity and that adds up to the artistic freedom to have FUN!!!"
- Leslie Perlis

A Message From The Artist

My work is a balance between large-scale architectural commissions and intimate personal works of art. I enjoy the challenge of large-scale architectural commission work, where the main goal is to combine diverse elements into a visually exciting, cohesive design that satisfies my artistic values, the purpose and architecture of the building, and the desires of the client. For example, a few years ago I received a commission from Temple Emanuel in Atlanta, Georgia (USA). The Rabbi had a concept to portray the 'cycle of life' and my task was to integrate that theme into the unusual zigzag shapes of the existing window frames. I love challenges like that and it is extremely gratifying to successfully provide the perfect solution.

The other side of my balancing act is my autonomous exhibit & gallery work that allows me the freedom to express visual interpretations of concepts, ideas and viewpoints that are important to me. Creating art gives me a way to work out how I feel about these issues and share my vision with others. It is also interesting to hear others interpretations of what they see in my pieces. Once I have defined my concept, the challenge is to figure out how to translate my ideas in glass. My current explorations in mosaic work allow me to combine all my past experiences with glass, including painting and fusing. I love to experiment with the endless possibilities of glass by originating new processes and refining old techniques to new levels of service.

I am delighted to have this opportunity to introduce my new work and processes in this book. I hope that my small contribution to the ancient art of mosaic serves in some way to expand the possibilities into the future.

My wish for you is also the sum of my artistic philosophy (see photo caption left) - keep it simple, be creative and above all have fun. - Leslie

The Roots of 'The Roots Of My Hoots'

When I was a kid my dad bought a '56 Caddie convertible. It was maroon, very cool and our family was crusin' before crusin' was cool. The legend was that Chuck Connors (who played the Rifleman on TV) had borrowed the car from its' original owner and somehow had burned a hole in the back seat with his cigarette ash. My Dad took great pleasure recounting that story to explain why two of the 'tuck and roll' upholstered panels in the back were different. Little did I know how, many years later, that car would play a significant role in a major work of art that I would create (see photo left, more on page 44).

Where Do Ideas Come From?

People often ask me how I come up with my creative ideas. The honest answer is that ideas develop on a meandering path, one thing leads to another - life experience makes it interesting and technique makes it possible. The technical skills & processes that I use today just sort of evolved. A fabrication problem solved often leads to a newly discovered technique and the successful completion of a design inspires the next. Thinking back on it now I realized that my whole life is the inspiration for the sculptures presented in this book. My long and winding road through the various glass art disciplines prepared me to meet every technical dilemma head on.

I started doing traditional stained glass in 1971, very early in the contemporary art glass revival. I studied stained glass design with Maureen McGuire, Lutz Haufchild, and Johannes Schreitter. Along the way I learned about glass painting from Dick Millard & Frank Reusche. Then in the mid 80's I took a wild fusing class from Dan Fenton and Boyce Lundstrom and they really 'got me fired up' to begin a completely new direction. At first I thought I would incorporate fused pieces into my stained glass but I ended up creating fused wall installations, comprised of iridescent glass with anodized titanium woven throughout, using no lead came at all. Then I took some advanced fusing classes offered by Gil Reynolds and soaked up even more techniques. It wasn't long before I started to make some interesting fusing, casting and slumping discoveries of my own.

The seminal project that would lead me to envision **Dimensional Mosaics with Fused & Painted Glass Elements** happened in 2002. I received a call from the Brigantine Restaurant in Del Mar, California with a request for five stained glass windows. A typical project that quickly escalated into a vast mosaic mural that would take me down a new and extraordinary road (see photo above right, complete project on page 26).

I'd like to introduce you to my alter ego - 'The Roots of My Hoots'. This sculpture is an autobiographical life size work that is 62" tall by 42" wide and deep (1.6 m x 1 m). The imagery comes from my personal environment but the viewpoint is an examination of my life through the viewer's eyes. See pages 42 to 47 for more details.

The 'Dimensional Mosaics' Process in a Nutshell

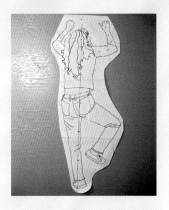

Are you ready to take the Next Step?

The process of how I create my Dimensional Mosaic sculptures is very straightforward. Here are my 10 basic steps from concept to completion. Don't worry I'm not going to leave you hanging, you will find complete step-by-step instructions on the pages that follow.

1. Decide what I want the focus of the sculpture to be (subject, theme, activity, premise, emotion, etc).

2. Do a rough sketch of my basic idea then find a willing model to pose for some conceptual pictures (page 8).

3. Select and print the photo, perhaps after some computer manipulation, then make a pencil tracing of the outline and the major components using a sheet of tracing paper (see an example of this on page 8).

4. Make several photocopies of this tracing then add and refine the details of the work (see page 8).

5. Enlarge the sketch to full-size (photo top left). Watch a video outlining several enlarging techniques on the Next Step website: www.nextstepartglass.com

6. Transfer the full-size drawing outline to a sheet of plywood then use a jigsaw to cut it (see page 9). Sand and seal the plywood with Kilz™ primer (see page 10).

7. Transfer the major inside design lines to the full-size cutout to use as placement guides. Use both the smaller detail sketch & the full-size drawing to determine the specific interior elements (see page 10).

8. Now the fun part. Select, create, enhance and add the design elements to the sculpture. I like to segment my sculpture into a few sections, i.e. the head, the shirt, the pants, allowing me to work in stages (see page 13).

9. When I have completed components for a section, I glue that section to the plywood base (but I don't grout it yet). Then I move to the next section, create the components and glue those to the base. Continue in this way until all mosaic pieces are attached to the base.

10. The final step is grouting. I normally use several colors of grout in my sculptures depending on the effect I want to achieve. Planning and execution of this step is a key element (see pages 11, 19 & 20).

Tools & Equipment

- Power-saws for woodworking (jigsaw, table-saw, circular-saw)
- Glasscutter & Grozing pliers
- Glass grinder
- Glass saw (with rigid-wire blade)
- Ceramic tile cutter/breaker
- Fusing Kiln & all related supplies
- Blazer (propane) torch
- Heat protective gloves
- Safety glasses, Rubber gloves
- Adhesive bandage (Band-Aid™)
- Good music (a girls gotta' dance!)

Materials & Ingredients

- Drawing / Creative Necessities:
  - Pencil (soft lead is best)
  - Ruler / drafting curves
  - Tracing paper (aka onion skin)
  - Photos for inspiration
- 3/4" or 1" (2 or 2.5 cm) plywood
- Sealer paint, primer (i.e. Kilz™)
- Tile grout, various colors
- Masking & clear tape
- Adhesives:
  - White glue (i.e.Weldbond™)
  - Silicone sealant, clear
  - Thinset tile adhesive
  - UV curing glue
- Fusible glass (all fusible components must have the same COE):
  - Sheets (textured, iridized etc)
  - Frit (assorted sizes and colors)
  - Stringers & noodles, (spaghetti, fettuccini, etc)
  - Dichroic glass (all styles)
  - Gillefiori slices (by Gil Reynolds)
- Non-fusible glass:
  - Textured (colored & clear)
  - Blown antique glass
  - Found or salvaged glass
  - Glass jewels & nuggets
- Chocolate, especially M&M's (a girl's gotta' snack!)

Mosaic Components

- Italian mosaic tiles (tessera & smalti)
- Preshaped glass elements:
  - Cast, pressed, torchworked
  - Commercial cuts (waterjet, Wasser™, formed)
  - Dichroic shapes
  - Globs, nuggets, marbles
  - Roundels, bevels, jewels
  - Millefiori slices
- Ceramic tiles (old or new)
- Beads (all shapes and sizes), can be glued elements or strung and dangled from the work
- Faceted elements (glass, crystals, cubic zirconia, vintage jewels)
- Metal or non-glass components
- Found objects of all types (ceramic, stone, glass, seashells, etc.)
- Whatever inspires you

Things You Make or Buy

- Cane slices (fused & fire polished)
- Frit-cast shapes (Freeze & Fuse™)
- Hand painted detail pieces
- Rubber stamp painted pieces
- Beads, torch made
- Beads, fused
- Beads, commercial
- Cut pieces of sheet glass
- Fused glass components
- Slumped glass components
- Shaped stringers & noodles (formed with a Blazer torch)
- Multi-colored twists (made with bead torch or blazer torch)
- Fancy shapes & groove cuts (made with rigid-wire diamond blade saw)
- 3D build-ups (multi-layer fused and slumped glass)
- Frames, wood or metal, decorated & repurposed
- Grout as a design element, from fine lines to major sections

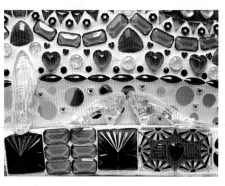

Detail from the sculpture 'Crown' (see page 34) showing widespread use of faceted glass jewels, cane slices, and 'crystal slippers' (once owned by a certain princess?).

This sculpture features salvaged guitar tuning pegs, a cloth guitar strap decorated with glass elements and extensive rubber stamped details on the neck (see page 28).

Project Imagery Development

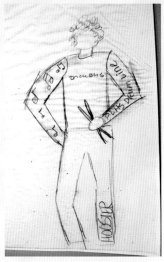

Evolution of a Design for my 'Stix' Sculpture

I have an ever-increasing list of project concepts and visual effects I would like to accomplish. I usually start by making a list of my ideas and then do some rough sketches. I wanted to add a third figure to my family of life size mosaic figures. I conceived this 'Stix' project so I could use my son Eric Pratt as my subject. He has lots of interests and I knew it would be fun to portray. I did a quick sketch of the pose I wanted (photo top left) then I persuaded Eric to do a photo session with me (he had no idea of what I was up to). I picked over all my photos and chose the pose I liked best (photo top right).

I used my desktop computer to size this image to fit on a standard sheet of paper then printed it out. Then I trace the major design lines from the printed photo onto a sheet of tracing paper (photo middle left). Tracing paper is my friend (don't worry I have other friends as well) I have it in sheets of various sizes and in long, wide rolls. I use a light box or tape the photo and tracing paper onto a window and use the natural light to help me see the image. I trace the image in pencil first, make my refinements then finalize using a fine tip marker.

Next I place a new sheet of tracing paper on top and begin to add design details (photo middle right) or sometimes I make photocopies of the original tracing. I like to try different ideas and design combinations and always end up with several versions. Often I'll create a design element that I like but it may not be in the correct location. I simply trace that element onto a separate piece of onionskin, then cut and place it exactly where I want it. That's how I moved the drum from the figure's hip (photo middle right) to his chest (photo lower left).

The final design step is to colorize. I like to use brush pens with waterbased inks (i.e. Tombow™) or colored pencils but you could use watercolors, colored markers or any coloring technique that you prefer. If my project is three-dimensional, such as the 'Roots of my Hoots', I make a 3-D model (called a maquette) from my original tracing sketch to see how each side will look standing up (see photos on page 43). When I am satisfied with the outline shape of the base component I follow the same design steps for each surface of the sculpture.

Her Escape Recalled Several Harrowing Events

From this point forward I will use my 'Escape' sculpture to illustrate the technique that I use to create these art pieces. Use the refined small-scale design (similar to the one we completed on the previous page) to create the full-size pattern. There are several ways to enlarge a design. You could draw it freehand if you possess that talent, use the grid enlarging technique, use an enlarging photocopier and tape the sections together, use an opaque projector to project and trace, or scan it into a computer enlarge it to full-size and have a quick print service print it out on their oversize printer. Watch a video covering all these enlarging techniques on the Next Step website. www.nextstepartglass.com

Once you have the full-size drawing, use a large sheet of tracing paper to trace over the full-size design (I buy tracing paper on a roll, but you could tape several pieces together from a pad). Trace the overall outline first, then trace the major break lines for each design section (see photo top right). I don't fill in every detail on this full size drawing. Instead I segment the design into its major components and create a more detailed drawing for each section on separate pieces of tracing paper. I use these sectional detail drawings to help me make glass and component choices and also to serve as the full-size patterns for my glass shapes.

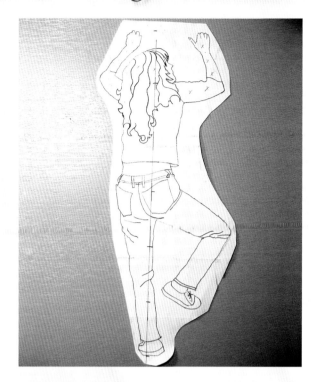

Fabricating the Structural Base

Depending on the size of my piece, I will use 1/2", 3/4" or 1" (13, 20 or 25 mm) thick plywood for my structural base. For this life-size figure project I'll use 1" (25 mm) plywood. Turn the full-size tracing paper drawing over (back side up) and use a soft lead pencil (a 314 drafting pencil or a 3B lead pencil) to retrace all the design lines on the backside of the pattern. Now turn the pattern right side up, tape it to the plywood and use a burnisher (a pointed stick) or a pencil to retrace the outside perimeter line only. The soft lead pencil line will transfer from the tracing paper onto the wood (photo middle right).

Use a jigsaw to cut the plywood following the outline. A jigsaw is quite simple to operate but I must confess that I call my friend Tim Pratt for his expertise in this area (he's a general contractor). The next step is to paint the plywood, front, back and all edges with two coats of white primer paint, I like to use Kilz™ primer (see photos on page 10). The mosaic adhesive sticks better to the sealed wood and the white base enables any transparent or semi-clear glass colors to show up better.

Design, Color and Create - The Fun Part

Allow the primer to dry completely, then place the full-size drawing right side up on your plywood cutout and tape it down. Now transfer the major inside design lines from the drawing to the painted wood using the same burnish technique as we used for the previous step (page 9). See the finished base in photo at lower left.

Now we can start making some design decisions. I like to use a great variety of materials in my sculptures such as ready made glass tiles (i.e. tessera, smalti, sintered, cast), my own fused glass elements, glass frit, old jewelry, glass beads, broken ceramic plates, stuff I find in recycle bins (aka trash), the list goes on. The part I enjoy the most is making my own custom glass elements (see photo below). I embellish them with stringers, paint, frit, pattern slices, dichroic, whatever I can find that is COE compatible.

I also use non-fusible stained glass that I embellish with fired-on glass paint, either hand applied or with a rubber stamp. I also have a wonderful collection of found glass treasures I have been gathering forever that includes cast pieces, torch-worked items, vintage & new jewels and other curious objects (I used a great variety of components in the girl's shirt on next page).

This is the backside of the 'Roots Of My Hoots' sculpture (see page 42). The hair was created with a multi-layer stack, similar to the process described on page 13. The shirt features an iridescent background with cosmic symbols of the earth, sun, planets, and stars. Symbolizing where we live and that we need to protect it and realize that we are a part of something bigger.

Grout as a Design Element

An often overlooked but exceptionally important element in my pieces is the grout areas. Applying the grout is the last step of my process but allowing space for the grout is a decision that must be made during the design phase. If you look carefully at the finished sculptures in this book you will notice how the grout plays a significant role in the design. Some places the grout lines are very thin while other places the grout encompasses a large area. Sometimes I will color the grout to match the glass around it for a more painterly quality while other times the grout is a contrasting color to emphasize the glass details. Look at the torso of the figure shown at right. Notice how the light blue grout on the left side takes up almost as much area as the glass does. In addition the light blue color contrasts and emphasizes the blue glass nuggets, the cast moon & star pieces and the fused star circle. Now examine the thin red grout line around the bottom half of the fused heart circle, around the fingers of the hand and some lines in the arm on the right. The color is almost an exact match to the red shirt glass and the grout virtually disappears.

Pattern Creation

I like to create my cut-shape patterns on the fly rather than make them all at once. This gives me flexibility to alter my design as the inspiration hits me. I place one of the sectional detail drawings that I made on tracing paper (see page 9, second paragraph) on the corresponding section of the plywood base then tweak and refine the design to create the effect I'm looking for.

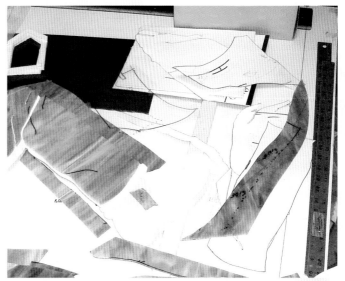

I tend to use opaque glass for most sections of my mosaic sculptures, (although there are times when a transparent color is the best choice, so I do not rule it out). Since I am using mostly opaque glass I transfer my design to card stock using a photocopier or sometimes I'll use the trace and burnish technique (see page 8, second paragraph) then I cut the patterns with standard scissors, a craft knife (Xacto™) or 3 bladed pattern shears (aka lead pattern shears) that removes a narrow strip of paper between the pattern pieces automatically allowing space for the grout line. Then I use a felt tip marker (Sharpie™) to trace the pattern to my glass. Do not create your patterns or cut your glass until you have read the ProTip - Finishing the Base Edge on page 12.

ProTip: Finishing the Base Edge

Before you cut any glass for your project you must decide how you are going to finish the outside edge of the plywood base. There are 2 good options to accomplish this.

1. The edge finishing method that I prefer is also the most meticulous. I cut, grind, and glue glass strips around the entire edge of the piece. These strips are of various lengths, depending on the curvature of the edge and sometimes I even fuse and slump an edge section for a special effect (see photo on page 33 upper right). I like to use the same glass that is on the topside, to match and extend the design around the edge (see photo above right). This means I have to cut and attach my topside pieces to overhang the edge about 3/32" (4 mm) allowing 1/8" (3 mm) for the thickness of the glass and 1/32" (1 mm) for the silicone adhesive. When I am using glass with a pronounced grain pattern, as show in the above right photo, I want to make sure the streaky pattern on the edge glass matches the adjacent piece on the top surface. I take care when cutting the top glass to leave enough glass to 'fold over the edge' so the grain pattern can fold at the correct angle. I cut and attach these edge pieces at the same time as the topside sections. This is a great deal of detail work but I think the result is worth it.

2. The other method is to paint the entire edge a neutral color like black, gray, white or some complimentary shade. Or you could choose a combination of colors that match up with the colors on the top side of the mosaic design. If you're going to paint the entire edge the same color it is best to do that before you start attaching any mosaic pieces. If you're going to paint various colors to match the mosaic sections you'll do that at the very end, after grouting and clean up. In this case I recommend masking the topside glass to prevent paint overlap.

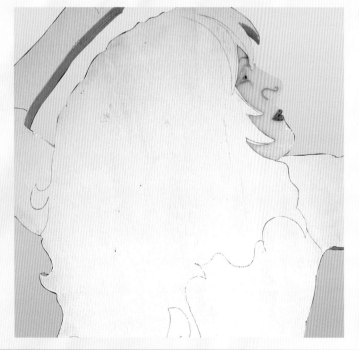

Please Face The Sculpture

I break my sculpture designs into smaller sections (see 'ProTip: Project Management' next page) and I like to start with the head section. Then I divide these sections even more. Here I have one glass piece for the face and 8 for the hair (see photo at top of next page). I love to create the face right away because a finished face seems to bring the sculpture to life. I selected a pink-flesh color glass for the base, then added some reddish-pink glass for the lips, a small piece of hazel with a black dot for the eye, and stringers that I shaped on a Blazer™ torch for the nose, brow and eye details plus a little black paint for the eyelashes (see close up on page 22). I tack fused the facial features to the base glass then placed the finished face on my wood cutout as soon as it came out of the kiln (do not glue it yet). The photo at left illustrates the life energy that the face brings to the sculpture.

ProTip: Project Management

I like to break my work down into smaller more manageable elements. For this sculpture I will start with the head section, then I'll move to the pants, then to the shirt and finish with the shoes and hands. Segmenting the sculpture in this way gives me an opportunity to watch my sculpture come together in stages. I get a wonderful sense of satisfaction and accomplishment as each section is completed. That in turn gives me a renewed energy and enthusiasm to carry on.

A Hair Raising Experience

The first pieces I cut are the 8 major glass sections for the hair. I wanted to establish a playful attitude so I selected an assortment of blues and greens for the base layer (see photo above right). I use my glasscutter for the simple shapes and a diamond wiresaw (i.e. Taurus Ringsaw™) for the more complicated shapes. In this case I had to use my wiresaw for the face and also for most of the hair. After cutting, I like to shape and refine all edges on a glass grinder, making sure to allow space for the grout. Arrange these pieces on the wood cutout.

Now I'll add a 2nd, 3rd, 4th or more layers of glass to the hair sections to produce depth & detail. I decided to add a spiral detail to several pieces to simulate hair ringlets. I drew the spirals directly on the glass (see lime green piece at center in photo) then used my diamond wiresaw to cut the detail. After all layer detail pieces are cut, grind and refine the glass edges. Secure these detail layers to the base glass using a few dabs of white glue and let it dry completely before moving them to the kiln.

Place all sections in your kiln on a prepared kiln shelf and fire using an appropriate tack fuse schedule. Some smaller pieces in this section are a single layer only. I put these pieces in the kiln along with the tack fuse sections, to fire polish and smooth their edges (notice these pieces in the front left area of the kiln shelf).

When the kiln has cooled completely remove the sections and arrange them on the wood base to see how they look (see photo next page). Look for the spiral cuts I made with the wiresaw (there are 9), notice how the color from the layer below shows through after firing.

A Sticky Situation

When all components for this first section are complete it's time to permanently secure them to the plywood base. This keeps them safely in place and provides a good reference as I make glass choices for the next sections. Occasionally one or two pieces in a section may still be in progress, depending on what those pieces are I may go ahead and glue all the other pieces and fit the missing ones in later or I may wait until everything is finished before permanently gluing down that section.

Make a Clear Choice

I have always used clear silicone adhesive for my mosaic sculptures, however many glass mosaicists depend on Weldbond™ white glue, Thinset™ white tile adhesive or other similar industrial strength adhesive. I prefer clear silicone because it has a thick viscosity, making it less likely to run and the clear doesn't have an effect on the color of any streaky or transparent glass that I might use.

Feeling a Little Edgy

If you've read the ProTip - Finishing the Base Edge (if you haven't, please read it now on page 12) you already know that I prefer to finish the wood base edge using strips of the same glass that is on the topside.

I cut the top and edge pieces at the same time. Then I glue on the top pieces and let them dry, then I fit the side pieces, trim their lengths and glue them on. Sometimes I'll tack fuse or paint design elements on the edge pieces as well (see guitar neck on page 28). It is usually necessary to tape these edge pieces (use masking tape) to prevent them from slipping while the silicone glue cures.

ProTip: Using Transparent Glass

I normally use opal glass for most of my mosaic sculptures. However there are times when a transparent glass is the perfect choice. Be careful to spread the silicone evenly over the entire back surface of the glass to minimize spaces and bubbles. If any silicone oozes out between the glass pieces as you push down, be sure to scrape it out using a small screwdriver or flat toothpick. Any extra glue in that space will prevent the grout from sticking in there later.

ProTip: Slumped 3D Components

It is fun to add some 3D components to these sculptures. I wanted to have a chocolate bar in one back pocket and a glasscutter in the other (these are 2 of my favorite things) and I wanted to hang a beaded keychain from one of the belt loops. 3D components must be slumped prior to tack fusing or the shape will not be as well defined. Create the mold-form by layering fiber-paper and/or fiber-blanket on a prepared kiln shelf, balance the glass on top of the forms then slump fire. The pockets on this sculpture were silicone glued to the base glass. The slumped belt loops were also glued to the topside of the glass after the flesh glass, the belt canes and the glass pieces for the pants were installed.

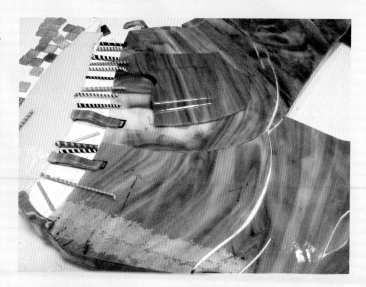

Pants Go On One Leg at a Time

The rest of my sculpture is created following the same basic procedure I used for the head. I had an extraordinary sheet of Wissmach™ streaky glass that I was saving for the perfect project and I decided it would be ideal for the pants. I carefully selected areas within the sheet that would emphasize the folds in the pants and enhance the movement of the legs. In addition I wanted continuity of color and streaks extending down and around the pant legs. The other consideration was my edge glass; it had to be cut from the same area of the glass to give the appearance of the cloth folding over the edge (see photo at right and also page 12 top right).

Notice how both back pockets and all four belt loops were slumped to get a 3D effect (photo below right). Be sure to read ProTip - Slumped 3D Components (top of this page) for details on how this was done.

Inside The Beltway

The wonderfully textured and multi-colored belt was created by lining up 70 pieces of thin cane twists, cut to belt width and arranged in a color-coordinated pattern. Thin twists are available commercially, but the ones I used in this project were hand made by my friend Heather Trimlett. The belt could have been created using a variety of streaky and/or dicrohic glass strips or even more simply from a single color. The glass edges would need to be fire polished.

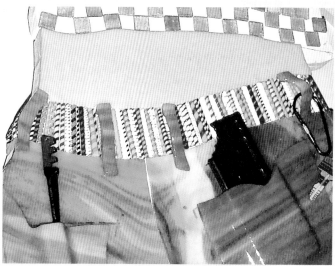

ProTip: Adding Movement & Depth

Take a look at my full-size drawing (page 9, top right) and you will see several crease lines in the pants, particularly on the left leg with some around the knee of the right leg. Graphic details like these are essential to elevate the sculpture to a professional level. These lines must be darker than the surrounding glass, like a grout line would be, but some of them don't go all the way across the leg so you can't simply create a new grout line by making that section into 2 pieces of glass. I have 4 ways for you to successfully create these very important crease lines:

1. Use tracing black glass paint to hand paint the lines and fire the paint onto the glass while you're fire polishing the glass edges.

2. Use a torch to shape black or darker complimentary colored stringers to fit your design shapes (must be the same COE), then tack fuse them to the glass while you're fire polishing the glass edges.

3. Use Liquid Stringer Medium™, a gel that is mixed with powdered frit (use a dark frit) and applied with a squeeze bottle or cake decorating funnel-pen.

4. My favorite method is to cut the lines into the glass using a diamond wiresaw (i.e. Taurus Ringsaw™) then fire-polish the glass sections. This saw-cut space will be filled with grout later, to create a contrasting line (see photos at right).

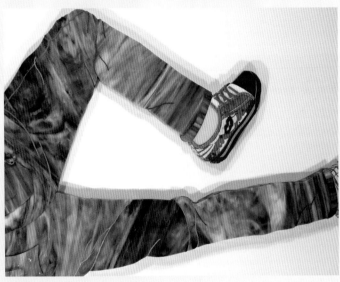

Keep Your Shirt On

I left the shirt until after I had the pants done because I wanted to use some Italian tessera tiles that I had left over from a restaurant job and I figured it would take close to 500 pieces to complete. These tiles have an alluring shimmer with a gold iridescence. They are precut approximately 1" (2.5 cm) square with smooth edges so they can be used as is. Of course dozens of them still had to be cut and shaped to fit into the spaces around the hair and to indicate the creases and textural flow within the sweater.

The first task was to create the flesh area that is peeking out from under her shirt (see photo below right). I used the same pink-flesh glass as the face and fire polished the edges. This piece was glued to the base before I started adding the smaller tessera tiles.

I could have created the entire shirt using only the tessera tiles but I wanted to take the shirt up a notch. I purchased some square milifiori tiles and some heart shaped beads that were about the same size as the tessera tiles, to intermix throughout the shirt.

I arranged the tiles to follow the natural folds of the shirt (information gleaned from the inspirational photo) to convey movement and form. Several tiles had to be cut & shaped to achieve this effect (see photos at right and on previous page).

The ribbed effect on the sweater-style cuffs was accomplished by tack fusing a fence-post row of amber noodles & stringers onto a base of COE compatible amber glass. The photo above shows the kiln setup for the cuffs and the photo at right shows them attached to sculpture.

The Feet (Shoes)

I frequently use clothes I have in my closet for inspiration, especially when I use myself as the model - which I did for this sculpture. I decided to take this work 'over the top' by adding my Peter Max inspired shoes (one of my favorite artists). I made the shoes using glass from 3 different manufacturers (all the same COE of course).

The top left photo shows the first phase of glass cutting and shaping for the figure's right foot. The next image is the setup in the kiln with the laces extended over the slump mold to allow them to fold them over the edge. The 3rd photo is the finished shoe installed on the figure.

The final photo shows the other shoe (the figure's left foot) fabricated using the same techniques.

The Hands & Wrists

The hands are the final piece of the puzzle (pun intended). The glass is the same flesh color I used for the face. It required extensive slot-cuts made with my diamond wiresaw to designate the details (see ProTip on page 16 for alternate methods). Red glass was added for the thumbnails and all pieces were tack fused and fire polished in the same firing.

The latticino bangle bracelet on her right wrist (the upper bracelet) is a slumped thick-twist cane. The bead bracelets, on both her right and left wrists, are comprised of torchworked beads (twist cane & beads made by Heather Trimlett). Notice how the bead bracelet on the right wrist was glued to the top of the flesh glass while the beads on the left wrist were set into the flesh glass.

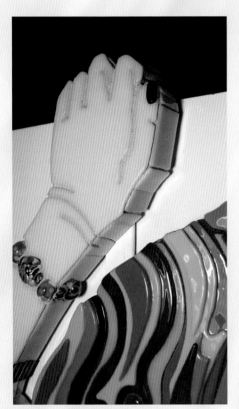

These images show the extensive use of grout line cutouts to create details for the sculpture's hands. See ProTip - Adding Movement & Depth on page 16.

Grout - The Finishing Touch

When the final mosaic piece has been placed and the silicone adhesive is completely dry it's time to fill the spaces with grout. Grouting really brings the sculpture into focus to sharply define the sum of all the parts. I like to use a variety of grout colors to either match the tiles or to create a contrast. If you look carefully at the photo below, you will see that there are 7 different colors of grout in that small section alone. You will find teal, yellow, white, orange, red, pink and of course the blue grout in the masked off sections. Most of the grout colors I use are available as standard premixed colors, sometimes I mix those ready made colors to make my own custom colors. Or you could add some grout tint colors until you get the exact color you're looking for.

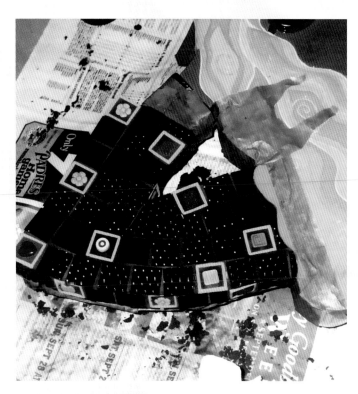

Begin by masking off all the areas that you're going to grout using a particular color - from larger areas like the sleeve in the photo at right, to short, single lines as indicated by the arrows in the photo below.

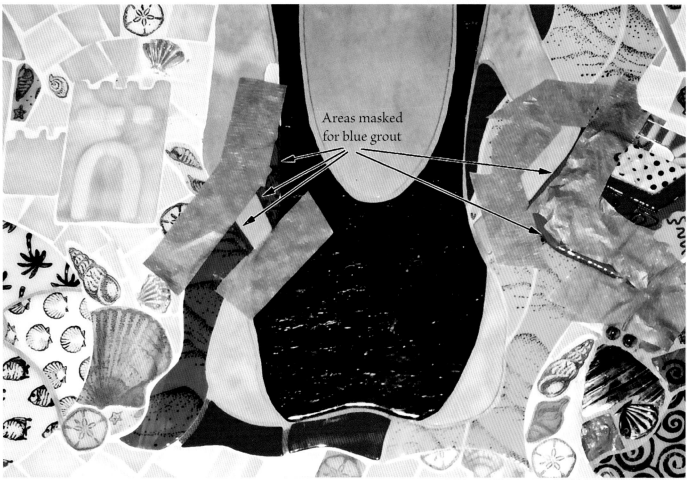

Areas masked for blue grout

Mix and Apply the Grout

Now the somewhat messy part, use disposable rubber gloves and cover your workbench with newspapers. Mix only a limited amount of grout to cover an area that you can finish in 10 minutes or less. I have found that an 18 oz (50 ml) plastic cup (a repurposed food container) - about half full of grout, is perfect. Put the dry grout in the cup , add a little water (and tint color if your using it) then stir with a chopstick. Add a splash more water (or dry grout) and stir until it is the consistency of smooth peanut butter. Place a dollop of grout on the tiles and use a small square of cardboard, a flexible plastic putty knife or your finger to smear it across the tiles, forcing it into the spaces. Work the grout into all the sections that you have prepared. Immediately begin the cleanup by gently wiping the newly grouted areas with a damp natural sponge. Do not wipe so vigorously that you remove too much grout from the spaces and do not swipe the sponge across any areas that you have previously grouted. Have a bucket of water nearby to rinse and clean the sponge between wipes. (I'd like to give a shout-out to Chuck Fitzgerald, a professional tile setter who walked me through grouting my first piece).

The grout will begin to dry and stiffen within a few minutes, at this point you can mold and shape it to fit around corners or to create a special effect. This is also the time to scrape out any excess grout or to clean out areas where you did not want the grout to go. When I have finished this first area I'll move somewhere else on the piece that I can grout without disturbing the wet grout. Mask off this area and grout with the next color. Continue this process until I have done all that I can before I must let the grout dry. Continue in this way until the whole sculpture has been grouted. Let the grout dry for a day then clean and polish with a dry soft cloth.

Dimensional Sculpting combining Fused Glass & Mosaic Elements

This photo is my finished sculpture 'Her Escape Recalled Several Harrowing Events'. I entered this figure in the 2006 Art Glass Competition mounted by the Art Glass Association of Southern California. This photo was taken in the show gallery and is exactly how visitors and judges encountered her. I was pleasantly surprised and very privileged to be awarded the Grand Champion ribbon for this entry. The glass art piece in the lower left of the photo is a fused and blown piece by Tim Harlan.

Her Escape Recalled Several Harrowing Events

Dimensional Sculpting combining Fused Glass & Mosaic Elements

Sculpture Size: 27" x 71" (0.7 m x 1.8 m)

Year Created: 2006

Shows Entered & Awards:

- 2006 AGASC Show - Grand Champion
- 2007 San Diego County Fair - People's Choice

Artist's Commentary:

Sometimes you just need to get away, get out of Dodge, flee, runaway, skip town, depart, you know what I'm saying. It could be to forget a big issue or perhaps you just need a change of scenery. That is exactly what is going on here. My girl is making her great escape over the wall, but not without taking her essential provisions with her, a glass cutter, a chocolate bar, and her house keys.

The title was a suggestion from the 'title master' himself - Mark Levy. When I am stumped for a great title I like to discuss ideas with my friend Mark, he always comes up with some zingers. I wanted to bring in the escape theme and the Hershey bar using a play on the words 'her' and 'she', as this piece is about her independence. The first letter of each word in the title spells HERSHE.

BTW: Be sure to get a copy of Mark's book 'Windows from a Different Perspective' by Wardell Publications - it contains over 100 of his eccentric titles and the spectacular stained glass windows that go with them.

Materials & Process Summary:

- Hair: multi layered fused sheet glass, grout line cutouts (hair spirals), see pages 13 & 14
- Face: torch shaped stringers, tack fused glass, glass paint
- Shirt: Mosaic tessera tiles plus millefiori slice tiles
- Sweater Cuffs: Amber noodles & stringers tack fused onto amber sheet glass to make a ribbed effect, see page 17
- Hands: Fusible pink flesh opal, grout line cutouts, glass bead bracelets & latticino bangle, see page 18
- Belt: cane twists, 3D slumped belt loops, glass bead keychain (all beads & twists by Heather Trimlet)
- Pants: non-fusible sheet glass, slumped pockets, grout line cutouts (fabric creases)
- Shoes: Tack fused cutouts, glass paint (bottom of left shoe, says "Got Sole?", right shoe says "Got Soul?")
- Candy Bar: Brown glass slumped over a fiber paper mold
- Non-glass inclusions: Fletcher Terry™ glasscutter (painted), house key (painted), Hershey Chocolate Bar (sealed), see detail photos on previous page

This sculpture was used as the example piece for the instruction section of this book - pages 6 to 21. Follow along with the artist as she explains how she created this figure starting from the plywood base cutout all the way to final assembly and clean up.

Artistic Influences:

- Peter Max, funky shoes
- Glasscutter, love of art glass
- Hershey Bar, love of chocolate
- I'd Like to stay and talk but I gotta go (escape theme)

Technique Reference:

- Tack fused ornamental cutouts, page 18 (top)
- Multi layered fused sheet glass, page 13
- Grout line cutouts, page 16 (top)
- Mosaic tessera tiles, page 16-17
- Bracelets (beads & cane), page 18 (bottom)
- Multi-color grout, page 19-20

Figure It Out

Dimensional Sculpting combining Fused Glass & Mosaic Elements

Sculpture Size: 27" x 71" (0.7 m x 1.8 m)

Year Created: 2002

Shows Entered & Awards:

- 2002 AGASC: Best of Show, 1st Place Mixed Media

Artist's Commentary:

Previous to this sculpture I had made several smaller figures in fused and cast glass and I decided it was time for me to make a life size glass figure. While I was in the process of figuring out how I was going to accomplish this, I was awarded a commission for the Brigantine Restaurant in Del Mar, CA (page 26). I created a mosaic wave for them that was the first large mosaic I ever made. I loved the effects that could be achieved and I decided it would be a great way to make my life-sized figure.

The inspiration for the pose came from a trip I took to the Children's Museum in Los Angeles when my son Eric was little. They had a dark room where the wall was covered with a light absorbing material of some kind. The idea was to lean against the wall in some crazy pose, then a bright light flashed and when you stepped away from the wall you could see the silhouette created from where you had been standing. Those 'frozen in time' images fascinated me and remained in my mind for many years.

For the most part my work reflects things in my life, my environment, clothes, colors and activities. This figure is no exception. She is a product of the casual San Diego lifestyle with a dash of Hawaiian flair. She is waving to the viewer with her Hawaiian and tropical fruit themed purse dangling from her arm (see more bags on page 36). I took a month to create this sculpture and I had fun thinking up ways to make her clothes. Her right pant leg (viewer's left) depicts the ocean that is only blocks away from my studio, the components include Italian tessera tiles, faceted gems, lampworked fish and cast seashells. She has on her cool Camper™ shoes with wild pineapple socks. Her left pant leg is a checkerboard of painted glass squares and roundels. Her belt is made up of lampworked peppermint swirl candies, combined with glass ladybugs. The shirt is Peter Max inspired with tack fused glass shapes, painted glass symbols, cast objects and dichroic patterns. The sleeves also have fun painted and rubber stamped designs and the dichroic sunglasses reflect a painted-on nostalgic beach scene (photo above right).

Artistic Influences:

- Peter Max, shirt & color scheme
- Travel, airplane, good-bye pose
- Hawaii, pineapple & tropical fruits
- San Diego lifestyle, sunglasses, palm trees, funky shoes

Materials & Process Summary:

- Hair: multi layered fused sheet glass
- Face: tack fused glass, dichroic eyeglass lenses with rubber stamped glass paint
- Shirt: tack fused glass with shaped twists, stringers & ornamental cutouts, rubber stamped paint designs, vintage jewels (necklace), glass nuggets, cast glass objects i.e. fish, seashells, stars & moon, patterned dichroic cutouts
- Hands: Fusible pink flesh opal, grout line cutouts, glass bead bracelet (beads by Laurie Maddams), dichroic glass (finger rings)
- Purse: rubber stamped paint designs, cast glass jewels, handmade bead dangles, brass ladder chain
- Belt: lampworked candy & ladybug beads (purchased),
- Pants: rubber stamped paint designs, glass roundels, cast jewels, glass nuggets, cast glass objects i.e. fish & seashells, tessera tiles (some with rubber stamped paint)
- Shoes & Socks: fire-polished glass, rubber stamped paint designs

Technique Reference:

- Tack fused ornamental cutouts, page 18 (top)
- Multi layered fused sheet glass, page 13
- Grout line cutouts, page 16 (top)
- Mosaic tessera tiles, page 16-17
- Bracelets (beads & cane), page 18 (bottom)
- Multi-color grout, page 19-20

Brigantine Restaurant Project

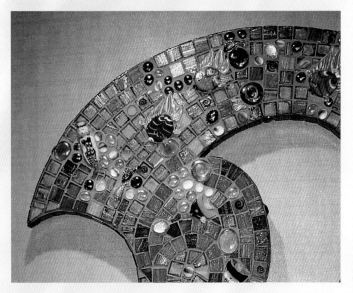

Dimensional Sculpting combining Fused Glass & Mosaic Elements

Sculpture Size: 2' to 4' x 45' (0.6 m to 1.2 m x 13.7 m)

Year Created: 2002

Artist's Commentary:

I received a call from one of my favorite clients, Barbara Morton, co-owner with her husband Mike of the Brigantine Restaurant chain. She called to tell me they were remodeling the Del Mar location and since I had done several stained glass projects for them in the past she wanted me to make five stained glass panels to insert into existing windows. My first thought was some sort of wavy leaf design for the windows. During my discussions with Barabra, we were trying to figure out something to put on the walls between the windows. One idea led to another until the 'leaf' part of my design was set aside and the five small windows turned into a 45' (13.7 m) 'wavy' mosaic sculpture that would cover 3 walls with the design flowing seamlessly across the windows.

I created a scale drawing of my proposed design (see below right) and after it was approved I transferred the outline of the design onto sheets of 1" (2.5 cm) thick plywood. I had a carpenter cut the plywood wave shapes using a jigsaw then I sealed them with Kilz™ primer paint. I drew my design directly onto the white primer paint and Barbara had her tile setter install the mosaic tiles and glass castings following my pattern design. To expand on the undersea theme I interspersed some really cool cast and lampworked tropical fish, seashells, mermaids, and seahorses into the tiles. Then I decided to use a sea green grout color that would match and compliment the tiles.

The wave design had to continue across the five window openings (the original commission). I used clear UV glue to adhere the tessera tiles, the tropical fish and the glass jewels directly to 3/16" (5 mm) thick clear semi-antique glass (see ProTip this page at right). I added a few darker opalescent glass shapes to accentuate the wave movement along with some circles that I had decorated with painted swirl motifs. I could have grouted between the mosaic pieces on the glass but I decided that I wanted the windows to be as translucent as possible so I cut and shaped the glass to fit very closely together in order to minimize the space (see photo top right).

This project was the start of the mosaic frenzy that followed, resulting in the creation of my life size figures.

ProTip: UV Glue Workflow

UV glue cures when it is exposed to ultraviolet light. The best adhesion occurs when the UV light passes through clear glass directly onto the glue layer. For this project I turned my full sized pattern drawing face down on a light table. Then placed the clear semi-antique glass on top and traced the design with a black marker (the marker is now on the backside in reverse). Then I floated the glass over my bench using some very strategically placed paper cups (or use blocks of wood). This way I could position my glass mosaic pieces the way I wanted them, then when it was ready I simply slid the portable ultraviolet lamp under the glass and turned it on to cure the glue.

Scale drawing of the complete sculpture showing the location of the clear window openings and both room corners.

Artistic Influences:

• James T. Hubbell (artist)
• Ocean waves, undersea life, nautilus shells

Materials & Process Summary:

• Plywood base, shapes cut with a jigsaw
• Tessera tiles and cast glass shapes
• Silicone adhesive to attach mosaics to plywood base
• UV glue to attach mosaics to clear sheet glass

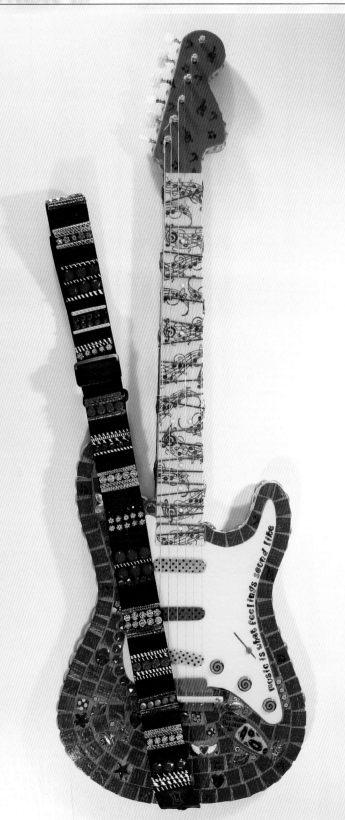

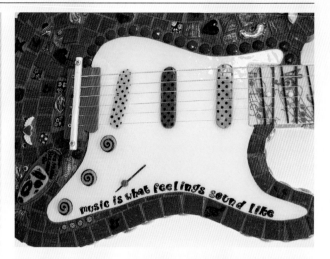

Dimensional Sculpting combining Fused Glass & Mosaic Elements

Sculpture Size: 40" x 13" x 2" (1 m x 33 cm x 5 cm)

Year Created: 2007

Shows Entered & Awards:
- 2007 AGASC Show: 3rd Place Mixed Media
- 2008 San Diego County Fair: 1st Place Glass

Artist's Commentary:

Music is an important and fun part of my life. When my son Eric was a freshman in High School I created some frit-cast instruments (sax, drum & keyboard) to benefit a fine art raffle for his school's music program. I really enjoyed the challenge of interpreting musical instruments in glass so I was keen to create an electric guitar using my dimensional mosaic technique. I settled on a Fender Stratocaster, the style that is played by some of my favorite guitar artists. I used tracing paper to transfer the outline along with the major components from a photograph of a real guitar, then I blew that up to full-size and made the plywood cutout. Most of the guitar components are made out of glass but some key parts are metal. The head features vintage 'mother of pearl' tuning knobs wound with actual guitar strings that are connected to the body using metal workings made by Terry Douglas (a metal artist who is my partner in several public art and commercial projects). The shoulder strap is also authentic but I 'turned up the volume' a bit by adding vintage jewels, beads, rhinestones and some of Heather Trimlett's glass twists. The guitar's yellow pickup board features a painted on saying - 'Music Is What Feelings Sound Like'. The rest of the body is red tessera tiles with a few red cast glass objects sprinkled around to add texture. The back of the guitar is also completely covered in glass. The neck is red with tack fused stringers and the body is black with a tack fused abstract design that symbolizes the explosive exciting sounds of the guitar. Both side-edges of the neck have cast glass hands with the names of some of my favorite guitar players, Carlos, Bonnie, Willie, BB, Wood, Jimi, Clapton, Keith, Chuck and Stevie Ray.

Materials & Process Summary:
- Guitar Body Front: Red tessera tiles with red cast shapes (jewels, hearts, stars, lips, dice, etc). Yellow pickup board has pinwheel knobs, painted pickups & words
- Guitar Neck - Top: Tack fused stringers for frets and yellow finger-position dots, rubber stamped musical notes, strung real guitar strings
- Guitar Neck - Side Edges: Cast hands with painted names of favorite guitar players
- Guitar Head: Vintage guitar tuning pegs, rubber stamped musical notes on head plate
- Guitar Back: Tack fused components with painted and rubber stamped details
- Guitar Strap: Authentic strap with added glass twists, rhinestones & pattern bar slices

Artistic Influences:
- Favorite guitarists: Carlos, Bonnie, Willie, BB, Wood, Jimi, Clapton, Stevie Ray (names painted on side-edge of neck)
- Fender Stratocaster guitar

Technique Reference:
- Mosaic tessera tiles, page 16-17
- Tack fused ornamental cutouts, page 18 (top)
- Multi layered fused glass, page 13

Reality Is Only Seen When The Mirror Is Clean

Dimensional Sculpting combining Fused Glass & Mosaic Elements

Sculpture Size: Entire Restroom

Year Created: 2006

Artist's Commentary:

I was given an opportunity to conceive an entire room design for a Southern California master bathroom remodel. My mosaic design evolved to eventually cover the floor and about half of the wall space. The vast majority of the mosaic components are ceramic but many of them were enhanced with fired on glass paint and rubber stamped details. The small shelving unit to the left of the sink mirror was a particularly fun aspect (see photo page 30). This was the original medicine cabinet in the previous bathroom. The door was removed and I cut a plywood frame to surround the opening, then created a mosaic design for the frame. The ceramic tiles come from the design on the floor and walls then I added some glass tessera tiles, some glass jewels and other cast glass shapes. Many of the tiles have rubber stamped details along with the painted phrase on the lower tiles that is also the name I gave to this entire art installation.

The large red & purple graphic design on the floor (photo lower right) is projected into the shower to interrupt the checkerboard pattern. The alcoves for the shampoo and soap (photo upper right) feature inspirational quotes that were added with glass paint, along with a cast glass heart. In addition to the mosaic I also designed and fabricated two stained glass windows for this bathroom (center right) that repeat and intensify the contemporary theme. Many thanks to Chuck Fitzgerald and Vince Molina for their ceramic tile setting expertise.

Materials & Process Summary:

- Cast glass components (ruby lips, winged hearts, etc.)
- Glazed ceramic tiles (with fired-on glass paint)
- Glass nuggets, faceted jewels, cane twists
- Rubber stamp designs on ceramic tiles
- Stained glass window panels

Technique Reference:

- Grout as a Design Element, page 11 (top)
- Mosaic tessera tiles, page 16-17

Artistic Influences:

- Have a beautiful day (printed on shower tile)
- Bright cheerful environment to wake up to

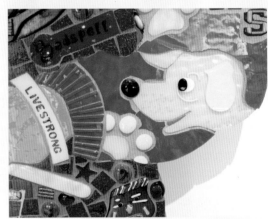

Dimensional Sculpting combining Fused Glass & Mosaic Elements

Sculpture Size: 27" x 71" (0.7 m x 1.8 m)

Year Created: 2004

Shows Entered & Awards:
- 2004 AGASC Show: 3rd Place Mixed Media
- 2005 San Diego County Fair: 1st Place Glass

Artist's Commentary:

In this piece I wanted to portray the interests of my son Eric Pratt and events in his life, including school, music, and entertainment (Eric was 16 when I created this figure) - see photos on page 8. Music is his life and he is an awesome drummer so I placed a drum prominently on the front of his shirt. The musical notation on his shirt was created using the grout line cutout technique, (see page 16 top) the amber color of the grout forms the music staff lines, the note lines and the treble clef. Symbols and logos are interspersed throughout that correspond to his high school (the dog and paws is the school's logo), his favorite bands, TV shows, theater shows he drummed in and movies. The checkered flags represent the Indy 500, where his dad is from and the palm trees with an ocean wave indicates where I am from.

The eyeglasses required a modification to the layered tack fused technique. I wanted the eye details to be clear & well defined so I cut the white parts using a thin opal and the colored iris from dichroic on black. Then I used a diamond bit in my Dremel™ drill to grind a small dot in the dichroic layer to expose the black for the pupil. The eyes, painted eyebrows, eyeglass arms (but not the lenses), nose, and lips were all tack fired to the base layer. Then the rimless lenses were created (see ProTip below) and tack fired in a separate firing allowing me to monitor it closely to ensure the lenses did not slump too far down.

ProTip: Layering for Effect

The figure in this project wears rimless eyeglasses. No problem you say, simply cut the lenses from clear glass and tack fuse them to the face. Unfortunately that approach does not come out looking the way you would hope. On a real person's face the rimless lenses refract the light to create a shadow around the edge. I simulated this effect by painting a thin coating of black glass paint on the outer edge of my clear glass lenses then tack fired the lenses onto the face in a final separate firing (see 2nd paragraph above, on this page).

Artistic Influences:
- San Diego, wave & palm tree; Indianapolis, Indy 500
- Music, drums, notes & symbols
- Musical styles, Musical Theater, Gomango Invasion Orchestra logo (group he plays with)
- My alma mater, Point Loma High School
- Assorted favorites, Music bands, TV Show, Hummer, Paintballs, Movies, Color red

Materials & Process Summary:
- Hair: multi layered fused glass, ornamental cutouts
- Face: tack fused glass cutouts, rimless eyeglasses (see ProTip this page), painted details
- Shirt & Pants: used smooth and textured backside of tessera tiles, tack fused glass, glass painted words, rubber stamped paint designs, grout line cutouts, glass nuggets (some duel colored), cast glass objects
- Shirt Neckline & Cuffs: stringers tack fused onto sheet glass to make a ribbed effect
- Hands: Fusible pink flesh opal, grout line cutouts, 'Livestrong' painted bracelet
- Shoes: tack fused glass, grout line cutouts

Technique Reference:
- Tack fused glass cutouts, page 18 (top)
- Multi layered fused glass, page 13
- Grout line cutouts, page 16 (top)
- Mosaic tessera tiles, page 16-17
- Multi-color grout, page 19-20
- Ribbed effect on neckline & cuffs, page 17 (bottom)
- Eyeglasses, simulated rimless lenses, ProTip this page

Crown - Don't Leave Home Without It

Dimensional Sculpting combining Fused Glass & Mosaic Elements

Sculpture Size: 38" x 33" x 2" (96.5 x 83.8 x 5 cm)

Year Created: 2008

Shows Entered & Awards:
- 2008 AGASC Show: People's Choice & 2nd Place Cold Glass

Artist's Commentary:

Every little girl wants to be a princess with an elaborate royal crown. This is my tribute to the Disney movies I loved as a girl, while discovering that fantasy often clashes with reality. The crown is an ancient form of headgear worn exclusively by royalty to symbolize victory, power and strength. These are qualities that we can now bestow upon ourselves. Sovereign crowns usually feature precious gemstones. My motivation was to honor the strong women in my family who taught me along the way, their images are featured in the crown spire centers. This sculpture is loaded with vintage & new jewels, cast objects, fused glass, sheet glass and glass paint.

Materials & Process Summary:
- Crown Spires (5 total): faceted glass jewels, (custom made) rubber stamped designs, cast glass objects
- Crown Circlet (upper): assorted faceted glass jewels, pattern bar slices, faceted hearts
- Crown Circlet (lower): 3D cast 'crystal slippers', assorted faceted glass jewels, small mirrored disks
- Crown Brim Ring: assorted faceted glass jewels
- Face: glass tiles with grout line cutout details (nose, eyebrows, bridge on eyeglasses), fused glass lips, rubber stamped paint designs on iridized sunglass lenses

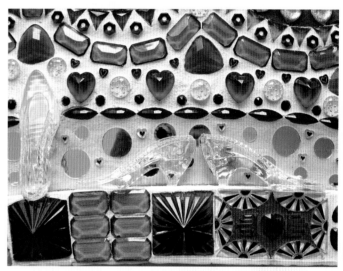

Technique Reference:
- Fused sheet glass, page 13
- Grout line cutouts, page 16 (top)
- Multi-color grout, page 19-20

Artistic Influences:
- Disney movies
- Sovereignty & Independence
- Power and Strength
- The art of Niki de Saint Phalle

As you can see in the photo at right, the Crown Brim Ring is built up higher than the rest of the sculpture. This was accomplished by cutting an additional piece of plywood to fit this brim area then this piece was glued to the lower plywood base prior to sealing.

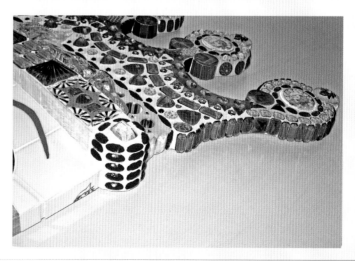

Bags & Purses

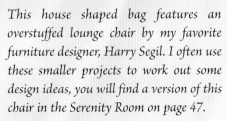

This house shaped bag features an overstuffed lounge chair by my favorite furniture designer, Harry Segil. I often use these smaller projects to work out some design ideas, you will find a version of this chair in the Serenity Room on page 47.

Here is another house inspired bag. This one has a raised section created by adding a thin piece of plywood to the base form. You can find a similarly shaped house in the Roots of My Hoots - Residential Bliss vignette on page 46 lower right.

This is a working purse - it is hanging off the arm of my 'Figure It Out' girl on page 24. It has rubber stamped palm trees, hula girls and flowers along with vintage glass jewels. Tropical fruit bead strings are dangling along the bottom edge.

Sculpture Size - Average:
- 6" to 8" (15 to 20 cm) wide
- 9" to 11" (23 to 28 cm) high

Artist's Commentary:

I love purses. The ones I make in glass honor the tradition of handbags as a very private supplement and personal enhancement for women. A purse is a symbol of independence for women offering the ability to carry whatever they may want and need, untold intimate possessions in the privacy of their handbags.

The style and size of our handbags is a reflection of our mobile lifestyle - we have more stuff to take with us from personal care cosmetics to the electronic gadgets that help us stay in touch and find our way. They are also a great way to display our personalities through the design, style, size, materials and colors we choose. I like to think of purses as 'portable works of art.'

The Dimensional Mosaic purses shown here are just a few of the glass purses I have created over the years. I started by making beaded, fused and cast purses but some of my life-size mosaic figures needed a purse to accessorize their outfits so I had to make several in this mosaic style. I really enjoy working on these smaller pieces. They come together much faster and I get to try out new ideas and processes that come in handy for my next large project.

Materials & Process Summary:
- Multi layered fused glass, tack fused glass with torch shaped twists, stringers & ornamental cutouts
- New & vintage beads, cast glass jewels, glass nuggets, cast glass objects, rhinestones, pattern bar slices
- Tessera tiles, dichroic glass accents
- Handmade bead dangles, brass bead chain
- Hand painted and rubber stamped designs, grout line cutouts

Artistic Influences:
- Purses and handbags that I own & see wherever I go

Technique Reference:
- Tack fused ornamental cutouts, page 18 (top)
- Multi layered fused glass, page 13
- Grout line cutouts, page 16 (top)
- Mosaic tessera tiles, page 16-17
- Multi-color grout, page 19-20
- Grout as a Design Element, page 11 (top)

Dance To The Beat Of A Different Drum

Metal dance floor and stand pole were created by Terry Douglas

Dimensional Sculpting combining Fused Glass & Mosaic Elements

Sculpture Size:
- **Red Hair Figure:** 35" x 65" (91.5 x 165 cm)
- **Indigo Hair Figure:** 18" x 65" (46 x 165 cm)

Year Created: 2005

Shows Entered & Awards:
- 2005 AGASC Show: Best Of Show, People's Choice
- 2006 San Diego County Fair: Best of Show, 1st Place Glass

Artist's Commentary:

Dancing is good for the mind, body and spirit whether you are dancing alone, with a partner or in a group. Dance is the joyous interpreting of music, moving to the sound in your own special way, to the satisfaction of whatever mood you are in. These dancers are having a blast. One of them is clearly more exuberant, wearing brighter colors while the other is more restrained with less flamboyant clothes.

The flashier dancer has wild colored hair with red and orange multi layered fused glass. Her shirt has various patterns & textures of fused, painted and dichroic glass with the saying 'Wear your art on your sleeve'. The pants are 1" (2.5 cm) squares cut from a single sheet of Kokomo Opalescent Glass interspersed with cast glass shapes. The belt and pant cuffs were made using vintage beads. I like blending old and new items for an interesting look and to honor the traditions of our craft. My favorite component is her high top Converse shoes - glass versions of shoes right out of my closet.

The dancer with indigo hair has a shirt made of tessera tiles and fused glass with painted designs and millefiori beads. Her pants were also cut from a beautiful sheet of Kokomo opalescent glass with several grout line cutouts and ornamental glass shapes. Her blue belt is a picket-fence line of vintage faceted glass jewels. You can just get a glimpse of her red socks peeking through the cutouts in her classic Steve Madden shoes.

Artistic Influences:
- Dancing is good for body, mind and spirit
- Life itself is a dance, the goal is to enjoy the journey - the destination is irrelevant
- Different styles and interpretation of dancing to suit the different moods of the dancer
- Clothing as a personal artistic statement

Materials & Process Summary:
- Hair: multi layered fused glass
- Face: tack fused glass, paint (eyebrows & lashes)
- Hands: Fusible pink flesh opal, fused red for fingernails, grout line cutouts, bracelets (and necklace) created from Heather Trimlet's handmade beads & twists
- Shirts: mosaic tessera tiles, tack fused glass with ornamental cutouts, glass painted words, rubber stamped paint designs, grout line cutouts, torch shaped stringers, Gillefiori slices, waterjet cut shapes, Bullseye fish scale iridized glass, glass nuggets, cast glass objects
- Belts & Pant Cuffs: vintage faceted glass jewels, cast glass objects, and cane slices
- Pants: Non-fusible Kokomo opalescent streaky glass, grout line cutouts, hand painted and rubber stamped paint designs, faceted glass jewels, cast glass objects
- Shoes: tack fused glass, Uroboros fibroid texture, grout line cutouts, Wasser glass heart cutouts

Technique Reference:
- Tack fused ornamental cutouts, page 18 (top)
- Tack fused glass cutouts, page 18 (top)
- Multi layered fused glass, page 13
- Grout line cutouts, page 16 (top)
- Mosaic tessera tiles, page 16-17
- Bracelets (beads & cane), page 18 (bottom)
- Multi-color grout, page 19-20
- Grout as a Design Element, page 11 (top)

A (is for Adrienne)

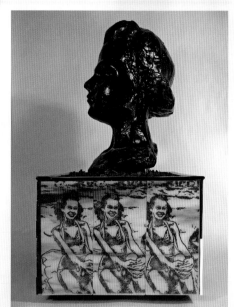

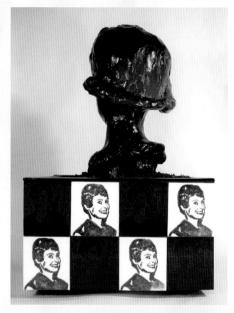

I named this art piece 'A' for my mother Adrienne. I started with a clay sculpture that my father created in the 1950.s. I decided to make a Dimensional Mosaic base that would be an attractive mount but would also add my own artistic signature to expand the scope and meaning of the sculpture as a whole.

Sculpture Size: 14" x 9" x 7 1/2" (35.5 x 23 x 19 cm)

Base Size: 9" x 7" x 5 1/2" (23 x 18 x 14 cm)

Head Size: 8 1/2" x 5" x 5" (21.5 x 13 x 13 cm)

Year Created: 1958 and 2008

Artist's Commentary:

This piece is a tribute to Adrienne and David Perlis - my mom and dad. My dad had a knack for several art disciplines and in the 1950's he created an interesting clay sculpture of my mother. Then for the next 50 years since this sculpture was created, it was moved from one place to another until it eventually ended up in my studio. It was badly cracked and a little worse for wear but it was an intriguing piece that held sentimental value for me. I decided that it would be a real thrill for me to honor my father by collaborating with his artwork to create an enhanced tribute piece of my mother.

The clay sculpture had some serious cracks, so the first step was to seek the advice of T. J. Dixon - an experienced clay artist who showed me how to restore and repair it. Then I created a wood base using 1" (2.5 cm) thick plywood and painted it with wood sealer. I have lots of family photos so I had the idea to create a series of glass tiles using images from the same era when my dad created his sculpture. I scanned the photos into my computer and manipulated them to create the images that I wanted. Then I ordered custom-made rubber stamps using my images. Finally I stamped the images of my mother onto the glass using glass paint then fired them in a kiln.

My nostalgic photo tiles cover most surfaces of the sculpture base, except on the front side where I also used some streaky Italian tessera tiles. The pedestal feet on the base are frit cast glass candies that recall a favorite family treat. The final touch is the mouth-watering scent emanating from the cocoa bark chips that encircle the clay head the in upper pan of the sculpture base.

Artistic Influences:

• My dad's keenness and enthusiasm for art
• Remembrances of my mom & dad

The original clay sculpture created by David Perlis in the 1950's had a number of severe cracks that had to be repaired before it could be used. After the cracks were filled the clay sculpture was sealed with several coats of clear glossy finish.

Materials & Process Summary:

• Base: mosaic tessera tiles, photographic transfer onto glass, fire polished strips (top edge), frit cast glass (feet)

Technique Reference:

• Mosaic tessera tiles, page 16-17

Sculpture Size: 42" x 42" X 62" (1 x 1 x 1.6 m)

Year Created: 2003

Shows Entered & Awards:
- 2003 AGASC Show: Best of Show & People's Choice
- 2004 San Diego Fair: Best of Show & 1st Place Glass

Artist's Commentary:

I'd like to introduce you to my alter ego - the Roots of My Hoots. I had been refining my contemporary mosaic style that started with my commission for the Brigantine Restaurant (see page 26). As my process evolved I began to feel a strong desire to create something on a grand scale. My art imagery tends to come from my immediate environment that is influenced by personal interests and life experiences. This piece has all of that with the additional curiosity of having to look at myself from another person's point of view. Roots of My Hoots has emerged as the centerpiece of my exploration into the world of modern mosaic sculpture.

I had two main objectives for this piece. First I wanted to create an autobiographical figure that would be the focal point of the piece. Second I wanted to pull out all the stops and use as many glass techniques as I possibly could. I started with a list of ideas and concepts that I wanted to incorporate, a panorama of personal vignettes to classify and define the setting. I winnowed the list down to four main scenes: our family's 1956 Cadillac convertible, a sunny day at the San Diego beach, fantasy houses to inspire a joyous life and an interior room setting featuring my favorite furniture and art.

The first hurdle was to devise a sculpture with enough surface area to enable me to incorporate all these scenes. I could get the main figure and 2 scenes simply by using both sides of the plywood form. To accomplish that the viewer would need to be able to walk around the sculpture, so I had to find a way to make it freestanding. That led to the development of the interlocking base that coincidentally provided 2 more surfaces for my scenes. I always start by creating a scale drawing to work out the major components of my design. Since this sculpture was going to be freestanding, I decided to build a maquette (a small preliminary model) to help me visualize the work in 3 dimensions (see photos at right).

This 3 dimensional scale model is called a maquette. This one is approximately 6 1/4" (16 cm) high or 10% of full-size. I work out most of the details on this model, right down to the colors and the painted designs. Go to the nextstepartglass.com website to watch a video on how this model was made, then you can download and print these scale drawings to make a maquette for yourself.

Roots Of My Hoots - '56 Caddie Ragtop

This vignette features an authentic and sentimental replica of our family's 1956 Cadillac convertible. It is shown cruising down Coast Highway 101 from Los Angeles to San Diego with palm trees and the Pacific Ocean pasing by in the background. This was our family car when I was just a kid and I loved it! I wanted my copy to be accurate right down to the last detail.

This car was from the era when chrome was king and this one was loaded. I had to fuse and kiln carve more than 30 separate components for the chrome parts alone, including the hubcap, door handle, body and window chrome, bumper, mirror and spotlight. These components were all made using fusible clear then I had a mirror backing added to them (many thanks to Joe Sewell for an expert silvering job). I especially like how the hood ornament and the hubcap turned out. I used 24k gold luster for the Cadillac logo in the center of the hubcap and also for the side insignia on the fender. Ron Carlson, a judge for the AGASC Show, commented that he could have stared at the hubcap for an hour. The tiles in front of the head lights & bumper have rubber stamped seashells and a grass pattern. Hand painted swirls on the blue/green tessera tiles represent the ocean. Scattered throughout the background tiles you will find millefiori cane slices, cast glass fish, vintage cast beads and glass nuggets to add a touch of plant and sea life.

Dimensional Sculpting combining Fused Glass & Mosaic Elements

The ocean is a big part of the Southern California lifestyle. For me it provides a source of beauty, serenity, power, and consistency - the waves persistently come in and go out, no matter what is happening in the world.

In this vignette panel we see our girl at OB sitting on her multi colored beach towel protected from the burning sun by a red & orange umbrella. Her beach ball is nestled in the seashell filled sand with a majestic sandcastle nearby. The waves are crashing to the shore and about to engulf her designer purse and towel. The waves were created with green & blue tessera tiles, glass nuggets, cast and lamp worked fish and a cute little mermaid (see lower right corner in photo below). The swirling waves are enhanced with fused and painted sheet glass and a few pieces of hand blown iridescent glass. The sand is 1" (2.5 cm) squares of beige opal art glass and the fused sandcastle was made using the same glass so it would blend in. The seashell images in the sand and the beach ball are decorated with rubber stamped designs. Cast glass shells are also embedded into the beach area. The umbrella has hand painted designs with Wasser glass cutouts fused on and the pole is a Moretti rod.

The sky wraps around the sculpture in all four vignettes, to provide an element of continuity. It was made using a combination of light blue opal and white streaky opal. Some of the cloud pieces have ornamental swirl cutouts that were tack fused to the sky. The sun is an intricate multi layered fused glass construction.

Roots Of My Hoots - Residential Bliss

For me a house must be a fun place to live, to express my personality and inspire a joyous life. Several years ago I went to Europe to study the buildings of two of my favorite artists, Antoni Gaudi, in Barcelona, Spain and Friedensreich Hundertwasser, in Vienna, Austria. It was pure joy to experience their unconventional conceptions of space and decoration. Their creative tile work alone was amazing and I felt a strong desire to incorporate a similar sense of wonder into my own work.

This vignette features four architecturally distinct residences with brightly colored designs and uniquely shaped doors. Doors are an important theme in this section empowered by the adage 'When one door closes another opens'. The 1st house with a concave roof sports a round 'Hobbit' style entry. The 2nd building has a top round door that is framed with multi-colored glass dice, this door actually opens within the sculpture to invite entry into the Serenity Room (see photo below). The door in the 3rd building features a picket-spike top with a curvaceous edge. The 4th house has a more conventional rectangle door with a rounded-top transom window. Two of the houses have sentimental address numbers (the 2nd and 3rd) taken from places that I have lived.

This section is full of fun textures and vividly colored glass. I used nearly every decorative technique in my repertoire including fused glass with ornamental cutouts, dichroic, painted & rubber stamped patterns, nuggets, cane twists, pressed jewels, you name it - it's in there!

If you look closely at the sky you will see a lady in the clouds, reminiscent of looking for pictures in the clouds when we were kids. You'll see her just below the airplane and above the peculiar openings in the upper left side. By the way, those openings are the window cutouts from the Serenity Room (see next page).

Dimensional Sculpting combining Fused Glass & Mosaic Elements

Roots Of My Hoots - The Serenity Room

This room is filled with my favorite things. The step shape of the wall on the right is from a house I used to own. The white background is 3" (7.6 cm) glass squares cut from non-fusible opal alternating smooth white opal and ripple white opal (ripple side up) for a checkerboard pattern. Since this is an inside vignette I placed only a few sky tiles at the very top for continuity.

The interior design features a Harry Segil style overstuffed lounge chair with rubber stamped designs fired into the glass and grout line swirl cutouts on the arms. The welt for the seat cushion is a thick filigree cane rod. A retro rotary-dial phone sits on the nearby table. On the wall above the chair is a mosaic reproduction of my favorite Peter Max poster, painted and fused with a Moretti rod frame.

The opposite wall has a half-circle side table. A separate piece of plywood was cut and attached to protrude from the surface, then decorated with painted tiles and cast hearts. The table legs were fused, ground down and fire polished to get a multi-layered look, under the table you can see the 'secret' door that opens to the little houses on the other side. On the table is a Bob Kliss inspired vase, fused to imitate blown glass, with painted portraits, stringers, twists and cane slices. Beside the vase is a fused and slumped dish filled with lamp worked candies. The offbeat shaped window has cutouts in the plywood, enabling viewers to see through into the adjacent quadrant (see photo on previous page). The mullions are regally decorated with rubber stamped crowns and fleur-de-lis to remind me that I am the 'Queen of my Domain.'

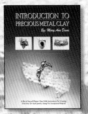

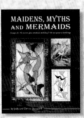

British Airpower Yea 2

ABOVE: C-130J Hercules of the RAF Air Mobility Force played a starring role in the evacuation operation from Kabul. (MOD/CROWN COPYRIGHT)

ABOVE: F-35B Lightning jump jets have deployed to Estonia to boost NATO's eastern defences. (MOD/CROWN COPYRIGHT)

ABOVE: HMS *Queen Elizabeth* and HMS *Prince of Wales* are now on call to respond to any global crisis. (MOD/CROWN COPYRIGHT)

ABOVE: Typhoon Watch. RAF fighter aircraft are on 24/7 Quick Reaction Alert. (MOD/CROWN COPYRIGHT)

LEFT: RAF Chinook helicopters are regularly called on to assist communities threatened by extreme weather. (MOD/CROWN COPYRIGHT)

ABOVE: Air policing operations with NATO allies bring the RAF into daily contact with Russian aircraft. (MOD/CROWN COPYRIGHT)

Editor: Tim Ripley
Senior editor, specials: Roger Mortimer
Email: roger.mortimer@keypublishing.com
Sub editor: Sheena Harvey
Design: SJmagic DESIGN SERVICES, India
Cover: Dan Hilliard
Advertising sales: Andrew Mason
Email: andrew.mason@keypublishing.com
Tel: 01780 755131
Advertising production: Debi McGowan
Email: debi.mcgowan@keypublishing.com

ISBN 978 1 80282 214 4

Subscription/Mail Order
Key Publishing Ltd, PO Box 300,
Stamford, Lincs, PE9 1NA
Tel: 01780 480404
Fax: 01780 757812
Subscriptions email:
subs@keypublishing.com
Mail Order email: orders@keypublishing.com
Website: www.keypublishing.com/shop

Publishing
Group CEO: Adrian Cox
Publisher: Jonathan Jackson
Head of Publishing: Finbarr O'Reilly
Head of Marketing: Shaun Binnington

Key Publishing Ltd
PO Box 100, Stamford, Lincs,
PE9 1XP
Tel: 01780 755131
Website: www.keypublishing.com

Printing
Precision Colour Printing Ltd,
Haldane, Halesfield 1,
Telford, Shropshire.
TF7 4QQ

Distribution
Seymour Distribution Ltd,
2 Poultry Avenue,
London, EC1A 9PU
Enquiries Line: 02074 294000.

British Airpower Yearbook 2022

The Royal Air Force (RAF), Fleet Air Arm (FAA) and Army Air Corps (AAC) are among the world's most modern and capable air arms, with proud traditions stretching back over 100 years of aerial warfare.

As the world's first independent air arm, the RAF has led the way in the development of aerial combat tactics, the strategy of air warfare, and military aviation technology. The Royal Navy pioneered the development of aircraft carriers and naval aviation, while Britain's army aviators have a distinguished history of service stretching back to the use of gliders to land troops in World War Two and the employment of helicopters in battle. Over recent decades, Britain's air arms have had to operate more closely together – either flying from ashore in joint task forces or afloat on aircraft carriers.

British Airpower Yearbook 2022 aims to provide an overview of Britain's current military aircraft, helicopters, and unmanned aerial vehicles, as well as profiling the major commands and units that operate them.

A major programme of re-equipment is underway for the RAF, FAA, and AAC and we look ahead at what these new aircraft, helicopters and drones will be able to do. The publication will also look back over the past year at major operations and exercises involving British military aviation, including the Kabul evacuation operation, missions

RIGHT: The RAF Air Mobility Force has a vital role moving the British Army around the world. (MOD/CROWN COPYRIGHT)

BELOW: 2021 saw the rebirth of the Royal Navy's carrier-borne air power capability with the Carrier Strike Group 21 deployment to East Asia. (MOD/CROWN COPYRIGHT)

around Ukraine and the Royal Navy's carrier strike group deployment to East Asia. It has been a very busy year with British air operations taking place over the world's oceans and above every continent.

Last year saw the publication of the British government's Integrated Review of defence, security, and foreign policy and this had major implications for the country's air arms.

It reaffirmed investment in a new British-made combat aircraft, the Tempest, to replace the RAF's current Typhoon fighter jets, as well as confirming the purchase of new Wedgetail airborne early warning aircraft, the new Protector unmanned aerial vehicle and upgraded Apache and Chinook helicopters, as well as a replacement for the veteran Puma medium helicopter.

This was the good news, but the high costs of modern military aviation technology means that the Ministry of Defence is unable to replace old aircraft with the same number of new ones. So, the active aircraft inventory of Britain's air arms is set to shrink to historic lows over the next decade.

Financial pressures have forced the RAF to even withdraw several aircraft types without replacement or accept gaps between old aircraft being retired and their replacements entering service. The RAF is having to accept a two-year-long gap in airborne early warning capability until the first Wedgetail enters service. RAF air transport capability is taking a hit with the retirement of the C-130J Hercules airlifter and there is also no replacement on the cards for the Sentinel R1 surveillance aircraft. On top of this the number of Typhoon fighters is

LEFT: Tim Ripley on tour to Kuwait in 2003 with the RAF Harriers of IV (AC) Squadron. (TIM RIPLEY)

to be cut by 24. The target to buy 138 F-35 Joint Strike Fighters has also been dropped.

The number of aviation-roled personnel is also to be cut in the drawdown of the British Army by 9,500 soldiers by the middle of the decade. At the same time, the RAF and Royal Navy are to lose a combined total of 6,300 personnel.

The Ministry of Defence says this loss of aircraft, personnel and aviation units will be compensated for by the fielding of revolutionary new cyber, space and information technologies

as part of its multi-domain operations concept.

In the Battle of Britain of 1940, the heroes of RAF Fighter Command who defeated Hitler's Luftwaffe were dubbed 'the Few'. Looking at the future plans for the RAF, FAA and AAC they may be acquiring more capable aircraft but there will definitely be fewer of them. A 'new Few' is taking shape in the 21st century.

Tim Ripley
Editor
May 2022

BELOW: The Eurofighter Typhoon remains at the heart of the RAF's air combat capability. (MOD/CROWN COPYRIGHT)

Ukraine War

British Airpower on the Frontline

RIGHT: Defence Secretary Ben Wallace headed around Europe in January and February 2022 on 32 (The Royal) Squadron BAe 146s to build a coalition to support Ukraine against Russian aggression. (MOD/CROWN COPYRIGHT)

BELOW: Defending the Eastern Front. In March 2022, 617 Squadron dispatched two F-35B Lightning IIs to Estonia to bolster NATO defences in the Baltic state. (MOD/CROWN COPYRIGHT)

On a freezing cold February morning a Royal Air Force BAe 146 aircraft landed at a Russian military airport outside Moscow. It was carrying Defence Secretary Ben Wallace to meet his Russian counterpart Sergei Shoigu in a last-minute bid to head off a war. Ultimately the Russian President, Vladimir Putin, took no notice of British diplomacy and two weeks later unleashed his tanks on Ukraine.

Airpower has been involved in almost every aspect of Britain's response to the Ukraine crisis after events have picked up pace since January 2022. On January 17 the first

RAF Boeing C-17 Globemaster headed to Kyiv loaded with a cargo of NLAW anti-tank missiles. More than 20 sorties were flown to Kyiv before the war started on February 24, to deliver some 2,000 of the missiles that would later be credited with devastating Russia's tank fleet.

On an almost daily basis, 51 Squadron launched one of its Boeing RC-135 Rivet Joints from RAF Waddington in Lincolnshire to head to eastern Europe to monitor Russian radio communications and radar emissions. These big jets could be spotted on open source tracking websites flying over Ukraine and the Black Sea in the build-up to the war. The intelligence they collected was partly responsible for the warnings from the British government that Russian troops were preparing to invade.

Russian naval movements in the run-up to the war caused great concern in London and other NATO capitals, so a major Allied effort was launched to monitor the Kremlin's fleet. The RAF's new Boeing Poseidon MRA1 maritime patrol aircraft played their part in keeping tabs on Russian warships in the Atlantic from their home base at RAF Lossiemouth in Moray and in the Mediterranean from the US Naval Air Station Sigonella.

The weekend before the war started, the UK, US and Canada withdrew their training teams and embassies from Ukraine to avoid getting caught up in any Russian attack. At the same time the British RC-135s and US intelligence-gathering aircraft stopped flying in Ukrainian airspace or over the Black Sea. Throughout the war British and Allied surveillance aircraft continued to fly in orbits over Poland, Romania and the Baltic States to monitor Russian forces in Kaliningrad, Belarus and Ukraine.

To protect them from attack by Russian aircraft, NATO started to organise a series of combat air patrols near the surveillance aircraft orbits. The RAF joined this effort, flying Eurofighter Typhoon sorties from RAF Akrotiri in Cyprus up to the Black Sea region. Airbus A330 Voyager KC2/3 aircraft refuelled the RAF Typhoons and Allied fighters during these missions.

NATO forces in the Baltic States were reinforced by the deployment of two 617 Squadron Lockheed Martin F-35B Lightning II jump jets to Amari Air Base in Estonia. This was the first time the UK's F-35Bs had operated from the NATO member's territory.

The Voyager fleet was called into action on February 10 to fly hundreds of Royal Marine Commandos to Warsaw for joint training with the Polish army. Once the war started they became involved in a covert training programme for Ukrainian soldiers to prepare them to use British-supplied weapons. A contingent of British Special Forces also deployed to eastern Europe on four RAF Boeing Chinook HC6s helicopters of 7 Squadron on the day the war started. They were spotted on flight tracking websites flying over Poland, accompanied by a pair of Army Air Corps AgustaWestland Apache AH1 attack helicopters.

The British and US governments were concerned that a lightning Russian airborne raid into Kyiv could lead to Ukraine's president, Volodymyr Zelensky, being captured. So London and Washington put their Special Forces teams in Poland on alert for a rescue mission. Zelensky declined the offer to be extracted saying, "I don't need a ride, I need more ammunition".

Watching Russia

RAF Surveillance Aircraft Patrol Russia's Borders

RIGHT: The last RAF operational sortie by Sentinel R1 was flown from RAF Waddington on February 25, 2021.
(MOD/CROWN COPYRIGHT)

BELOW: RAF RC-135 Rivet Joint missions go on around the clock from RAF Waddington to monitor Russian military activity in eastern Europe.
(MOD/CROWN COPYRIGHT)

Early on the morning of February 25, 2021, a Royal Air Force Raytheon Sentinel R1 Airborne Stand-off Radar aircraft took off from its home base in Lincolnshire to fly its last ever operational mission.

The V (Army Cooperation) Squadron crew of Sentinel ZJ694 headed east over the North Sea and were soon on task around the Russian enclave of Kaliningrad and close to Moscow's only European ally, Belarus. After switching on their powerful radar, the Sentinel's mission crew proceeded to collect 'product'

from inside Kaliningrad and Belarus. Russian and Belarusian airfields, missile bases, naval dockyards and deployed armoured regiments were all prime targets for the Sentinel's radar.

When the crew returned to RAF Waddington later in the day they parked up their aircraft for the last time. The squadron had completed a total of 32,300 hours during 4,870 sorties flown since the Sentinel entered service in 2008. As part of a cost-cutting exercise, the government had decided that Britain could no longer afford to keep V Squadron in

business and in December 2020 it put the five Sentinel aircraft up for sale. The US Army is now looking to buy the aircraft to beef up its own ability to monitor Russian forces in eastern Europe.

The demise of the Sentinel after a little over a decade in service, followed by the retirement of the Boeing E-3D Sentry airborne early warning system, or AWACS, aircraft of 8 Squadron in September 2021, did not mean the end of RAF surveillance

operations around the borders of Russia. The burden of this effort now falls predominately on the three Boeing RC-135 Rivet Joint signals/electronic intelligence (SIGINT/ELINT) aircraft of 51 Squadron and the newly delivered Boeing Poseidon MRA1 maritime patrol aircraft that have the job of monitoring Russian naval activity.

Given the rising political tension between Russia and NATO members, including the United Kingdom, it was not a surprise that Allied air forces and intelligence agencies were keen to monitor what the Kremlin's military machine was doing. NATO members in Eastern Europe, and partner nations such as Finland, Sweden, and Ukraine, feared Russian attacks after the 2014 Crimea crisis. So regular aerial surveillance flights around Russia's borders were an important part of reassuring key allies and partners that NATO was watching what was going on and was ready to help in time of crisis.

During the Cold War, spy flights around the Soviet Union and Warsaw Pact nations were a common occurrence as NATO members tried to set up a 'trip wire' of intelligence indicators to warn of a surprise attack. Today's surveillance flights have their roots in those Cold War missions, but modern spy planes are very different, and their technology is far in advance of that available more than 40 years ago.

Cold War-era surveillance aircraft included SIGINT and ELINT collectors to eavesdrop on Soviet electronic communications. Photographic reconnaissance aircraft regularly flew along the borders of the Warsaw Pact

countries to take sideways looking pictures of Soviet military bases. These planes were fitted with old fashioned wet film cameras that produced superb high resolution images of targets that often enabled to faces of Soviet soldiers to be recognised. However, the planes had to return to base to unload their film and develop the pictures. It was a similar story in the SIGINT and ELINT aircraft, with crews using old fashioned tape machines to record Soviet communications traffic and then bringing it home to be transcribed. This resulted in a delay of hours or days until analysts could actually see the results of the reconnaissance flights.

21st century surveillance aircraft are very different and far more capable than their Cold War counterparts. The digital technology revolution

means that the crews of today's photographic aircraft are able to access imagery instantly and email it directly back to ground stations or command posts while the aircraft are still on station. It is the same for SIGINT and ELINT aircraft, which are now able to download product so personnel in ground stations can listen in to potentially hostile radio traffic or monitor radar emissions in real time. The power of digital communication networks means that today's surveillance aircraft no longer have to return to base for their product to be actioned.

The sensors on modern surveillance aircraft are also optimised to monitor 21st century communications devices. Top targets are cell or mobile phone communications networks that require different types of SIGINT ➤➤

ABOVE: RAF Waddington has been the home of 51 Squadron's three RC-135 Rivet Joint signals intelligence aircraft since 2013. (MOD/CROWN COPYRIGHT)

BELOW: 51 Squadron has a long tradition of involvement in signals intelligence operations dating back to 1958 when it started flying missions around the Soviet Union. (MOD/CROWN COPYRIGHT)

ROYAL AIR FORCE   ZZ665

equipment to harvest new forms of information. Aircraft such as the Sentinel, have field radar systems that were in their infancy during the 1980s. These radars have two modes - Ground Moving Target Indicator (GMTI) mode that allows every vehicle moving across wide areas to be monitored in real time, and Synthetic Aperture Radar (SAR) mode that produces a three-dimensional image of tanks or artillery guns hidden under camouflage nets or parked in woods. The ability of the Sentinel or its US equivalent, the E-8C Joint STARS, to produce masses of intelligence and share it in a matter of minutes has transformed intelligence gathering and warfare.

The electro-optical sensors used on modern photographic aircraft are also massively more capable than old style wet film cameras. As well as their ease of distribution, this new generation of cameras have far more powerful magnification and, crucially, they never run out of film, so they can now image huge areas. When combined with GPS satellite navigation technology to imprint geo-location data, they allow interpreters to search through imagery far more quickly than their Cold War-era counterparts. Although much of the burden of photographic reconnaissance has been taken over by satellite imagery – as anyone who has attempted to look at pictures of their home on the Google Earth

website will know – it only takes a cloud bank to block imagery of certain targets for days at a time. This means that photographic reconnaissance aircraft have not been made redundant because they still have important role to play – taking pictures underneath cloud.

From surveillance aircraft transponder data published on flight tracking websites it is possible to follow many of the spy planes' movements. Their data shows that there were three main venues for NATO surveillance flights around the European part of Russia – the Black Sea, the Baltic, and the Barents Sea. In each theatre the surveillance flights took on a very different character.

Surveillance flights around the Black Sea were meant to reassure allies – NATO members Turkey, Bulgaria and Romania, and partners in Ukraine and Georgia – that they were not alone in the face of Russian assertiveness. US and Allied surveillance aircraft routinely flew around the coast of Crimea to demonstrate that NATO was watching what was going on.

In the Baltic region the surveillance missions were very different and focused on the Kaliningrad enclave. On a weekly basis, a combination of different types of surveillance aircraft could be seen circling around Kaliningrad over the Baltic Sea, Poland, and Lithuania. Keeping track of the exact position of Russian military hardware in the enclave was clearly a top priority for NATO.

Very different flight profiles could be observed over the Barents Sea, off the northern coast of Norway and Russia's Kola Peninsula. The submarine and naval bases of Russia's Northern

LEFT: Intelligence product collected during RC-135 Rivet Joint missions is analysed in the Air Warfare Centre's Thomson Building at RAF Waddington. (MOD/CROWN COPYRIGHT)

Fleet were the main target of these surveillance flights. The primary aim of these flights appeared to be to catch Russian submarines as they prepared to sail or were just leaving port.

From the data displayed on flight tracking websites it is clear that these Allied surveillance flights were not carried out at random but were part of a highly co-ordinated and centrally directed effort. Different types of surveillance aircraft, from multiple air forces, all appeared over the same pieces of air space at the same time to monitor distinct targets.

NATO repeatedly denied that it was responsible for directing the surveillance campaign. It appears that what could be termed as 'a coalition of the willing' had been established to organise the flights, under the loose direction of the headquarters of the USAF in Europe at Ramstein Air Base in Germany.

When the Ukraine crisis turned into a 'hot' shooting war on February 24, the RAF reconnaissance aircraft, along with those of other NATO air forces, pulled out of Ukrainian air space to the fringes of the Black Sea, out of range of Russian surface-to-air missiles. RC-135s of 51 Squadron continued to fly daily missions to monitor Russian communications. An RAF Poseidon was sent to Sicily to monitor Russian naval activity in the Mediterranean. Monitoring Russia suddenly became even more important.

BELOW: US Navy and RAF Poseidon MRA1 anti-submarine warfare patrol aircraft based at RAF Lossiemouth play an important part in monitoring Russian naval activity. (US NAVY PHOTO BY MASS COMMUNICATION SPECIALIST 2ND CLASS AUSTIN INGRAM)

NATO Air Policing

RAF Typhoons Forward Deploy to Romania

RIGHT: The Typhoon detachment in Romania on NATO duty has to be self-contained with engineers and other specialist personnel present throughout their four-month long deployment. (MOD/CROWN COPYRIGHT)

In March 2022 four Eurofighter Typhoon FGR4 jets from 3 (Fighter) Squadron arrived at Mihail Kogalniceanu Air Base on the Romanian Black Sea coast to begin a four-month long tour for NATO air policing.

With tensions high because of the Russian invasion of neighbouring Ukraine, this year's Operation Biloxi deployment looks set to be memorable. For its NATO mission 3 (F) Squadron is being supported by 150 RAF personnel based at RAF Wittering, forming the Headquarters of an Expeditionary Air Wing (EAW), as well as personnel from 1 Expeditionary Logistics Squadron and 2 Mechanical Transport Squadron.

The Romania mission is a long-established one for the Typhoon force. Last year IX (Bomber) Squadron flew to the Black Sea country for NATO duty. Wing Commander Simon Batt led that deployment and recalled what was expected of Typhoon pilots.

"With potentially hostile aircraft travelling at over 500 mph, it is imperative that we can react quickly and this is where the Typhoon comes into its own," Typhoon pilot

Batt said. "We can be airborne in a matter of minutes and then the raw performance allows us to rapidly climb to height and intercept the threat at supersonic speeds. I have been extremely lucky to have been flying Typhoons since 2005. The raw power and performance have always been phenomenal - flying the Typhoon still puts a smile on my face."

He continued: "Air Policing is all about securing the skies and reacting to threats immediately, wherever they are. We could be called to intercept an airliner in trouble or to meet a military

threat anywhere within UK or NATO airspace. The avionic system and sensor fusion allow us to have excellent situational awareness of all the civilian traffic, airspace constraints, cooperating aircraft (such as air-air refuelling tankers or other fighters) and target aircraft at all times."

In April 2021 Batt led his squadron to Mihail Kogalniceanu Air Base in Romania to stand 24/7 Quick Reaction Alert, or QRA duty, with their four Typhoon jets. This was the first mission to Romania for IX (B) Squadron, which had only achieved

BELOW: Russian military aircraft skirting around NATO air space are routinely intercepted by RAF Typhoon fighters. (MOD/CROWN COPYRIGHT)

Initial Operating Capability with their new Typhoons three months earlier.

The air policing mission centres on having fighter jets ready to be scrambled in response to suspicious air activity close to NATO airspace. "When the QRA alarm goes and we are scrambled your mind becomes completely focused," Batt said. "The pilots and engineers sprint out to the aircraft and then rapidly get the Typhoon started and airborne. There are myriad checks to be done and the whole team needs to work in concert to ensure we can get airborne safely and quickly. In some ways we are operating in a very similar way to a Formula 1 pit crew.

"Once airborne you are immediately assessing the tactical situation. What is the threat, what could its intent be, where is the aircraft of interest, what are the weather conditions, what civilian or military traffic could be in the way? Working alongside the ground-based battlespace manager, our job is to intercept the target aircraft as quickly as possible, without endangering any other airspace users.

"It is only after you have completed the mission, and are perhaps returning home, that you have time to reflect on what you have just done and the mission. I always get an immense sense of satisfaction after a QRA mission, knowing the combined effort of the whole team has once again delivered and maintained the air deterrence 24/7."

Batt described the QRA mission as a "bit of an emotional rollercoaster", with periods of intense and rapid activity mixed in with times of relative calm and long transits.

"As soon as the scramble alarm goes and you are sprinting to the aircraft the adrenalin kicks in," he said. "The heart rate jumps, but once you reach the aircraft your training takes over and you are completely focused on the task at hand. We work in concert with our engineers to get the aircraft started and

airborne in a matter of minutes to meet whatever the threat is."

RAF tactics and procedures are NATO-aligned and so flying the air policing mission in Romania is very similar to QRA duty back home in the UK. "The only real difference is the airspace we fly in," said Batt. "We therefore fly training missions to familiarise the pilots with the operating area ahead of any QRA missions.

"As the pilot, we are the final link in a long defensive chain of people and units. Our job is to intercept the target aircraft as quickly and efficiently as possible. We can then positively identify the aircraft and monitor its behaviour. We feed all this information back to our command chain so that they have the full tactical picture and can make informed decisions. The command chain has feeds and information from other sources that they can piece together to get a fuller picture of the situation; as a pilot we can only really see what is happening in our particular area."

QRA duty is not all action and running to scramble jets, though. Batt stressed that discipline and patience are just as important as events unfold. "At times we may be held on Combat Air Patrol for hours waiting to see if a threat penetrates our Flight Information Region – a piece of defined airspace that a NATO country looks after."

IX(B) Squadron is the RAF's newest Typhoon unit. It formally stood up at RAF Lossiemouth in Moray in April 2019 to be the service's dedicated QRA and aggressor squadron. In the latter role the squadron's pilots simulate threat aircraft during training missions flying against other RAF and Allies units.

NATO has been contributing to the enhanced Air Policing (eAP) of Romanian airspace since the 2014 Crimea crisis, when the Alliance decided additional assurance measures were required to protect its members on its eastern flank.

IX(B) Squadron's mission was the third time the RAF had deployed

ABOVE: Mission accomplished. A IX Squadron RAF maintainer inspects his Typhoon after a NATO air policing mission from Mihail Kogalniceanu Air Base. (MOD/CROWN COPYRIGHT)

to Mihail Kogalniceanu Air Base near the port city of Constanta for the air policing mission. Around 60 personnel from IX(B) Squadron were part of a larger 180-strong RAF contingent under the umbrella of 121 Expeditionary Air Wing.

Summing up the mission, Batt stressed the importance of all the RAF contingent working together. "This is a bit of a cliché, but we need the whole team to work effectively," he said. "We held QRA 24/7 and so we needed the caterers and support teams to keep us fed and warm; our communications engineers and battlespace managers to produce and publish the recognised air picture. Force Protection provided by the RAF Regiment while we were in Romania kept us safe; the operations team updated us with the weather and other aircraft movements; logistics personnel provided fuel and weapons; our engineers kept the aircraft primed and ready to go and the supporting ground equipment operational; and, finally, the pilots, who were there ready to fly. All of this was maintained 24/7 so that we could launch at a moment's notice to meet any threat. The whole team worked together to ensure we could get airborne in the fastest possible time, day, or night, whatever the weather. In this job time is everything; when you are travelling at over 500 miles an hour every second counts."

LEFT: Mihail Kogalniceanu Air Base on the Romanian Black Sea hosts RAF Typhoon fighters on NATO air policing duty. (MOD/CROWN COPYRIGHT)

Operation Pitting

Britain's Evacuation Mission to Kabul

For the last two weeks of August 2021 the world was transfixed by the humanitarian crisis in and around Kabul Airport in Afghanistan as more than 120,000 refugees were flown out of the city, including more than 15,000 by the Royal Air Force. The scenes of desperate Afghans overrunning the airport's sole runway and hanging onto the wheel wells of US Air Force Boeing C-17A Globemaster airlifters as they took off were harrowing.

In the first days of July the US and its allies closed down NATO's Operation Resolute Support, which had been providing training and advice to the Afghan military and police. The most high-profile symbol of this was the night-time evacuation of Bagram Air Base, which had been the main US base in the country since the invasion of Afghanistan 20 years earlier. British and other NATO troops held a series of parades around Afghanistan at that time to mark the end of their involvement in the conflict.

By July 4 only a battalion of 600 US soldiers and some specialist units remained to secure the military side of Kabul's Hamid Karzai International Airport, as well as the US Embassy compound in the centre of the city. Some 500 Turkish troops also remained at the airport to manage its security after the final Americans left. US President Joe Biden issued orders that US troops, contractors and the bulk of the embassy staff were to be out of Afghanistan by August 31 in time to meet his symbolic September 11 target to end America's involvement

in the central Asian country. However, tens of thousands of foreign nationals, aid workers and former employees of US and NATO forces remained in Afghanistan and few had even begun packing to leave or secured the necessary visas to travel out of the country.

This neat withdrawal plan looked good in Washington DC and in other NATO capitals, but it was based on the assumption that Taliban insurgents could be held at bay by the Afghan Army and Air Force. This proved to be a fatal miscalculation. Afghan soldiers saw the US troops leaving and started to vote with

their feet. Desertion sky rocketed and Afghan commanders started to negotiate local truces with the Taliban. By the end of July more than half of the country had fallen to the Taliban and the group's fighters continued their relentless advance.

In Britain's Permanent Joint Headquarters at Northwood, on the outskirts of London, intelligence officers and planning staff were watching events with some alarm and drawing up contingency plans. RAF liaison officers at the US Combined Air Operations Centre, or CAOC, at Al Udeid Air Base in the Gulf state of Qatar were already co-ordinating evacuation plans with their USAF counterparts. The main RAF airlift hubs in the Gulf, at Minhad Air Base in the United Arab Emirates and RAF Akrotiri in Cyprus, were put on alert to be ready to launch aircraft should the evacuation be ordered.

On August 12, President Biden agreed to recommendations from his military chiefs to send in three more battalions of troops to secure Kabul Airport to allow the evacuation to begin within days. In London the UK government came to a similar conclusion and dispatched 600 British paratroopers from 16 Air Assault Brigade to set up an evacuation processing centre at Kabul Airport. At this stage of the crisis both the British and US governments were still banking on the airport and Kabul city remaining in the hands of the Afghan military. They were planning on a steady stream of civilian charter and scheduled aircraft bringing the vulnerable civilians to safety.

This all changed during the evening of August 14, when Taliban fighters reached the outskirts of the city.

During the morning of August 15, the first Taliban fighters were spotted inside Kabul, prompting the Afghan President and other senior leaders to head to the airport. More than 40 Afghan aircraft and helicopters took off during the day and headed to safety in Uzbekistan.

Hours after the Afghan leaders had made their escape, tens of thousands of Afghans began swarming into the civilian side of the airport to try to get on any aircraft they could. Once inside the airport, they soon made their way onto the main runways, preventing any aircraft from taking off or landing. US, Turkish and British troops were sent over to try to clear the runway but not before hundreds of refugees had made their way on board at least one USAF C-17.

When dawn broke the Afghan civilians were still inside the airport and, more ominously, armed Taliban fighters had set up checkpoints around the perimeter. A new plan was now required.

Amidst the mayhem at Kabul Airport, US and British commanders had to come up with a new plan to get tens of thousands of civilians out of Kabul. The Americans »

reached out to the Taliban to find out if they would let the US and its allies continue to evacuate their people through the airport. Much to everyone's surprise, the Taliban said they would give them until the end of the month to complete their evacuation.

The RAF, along with the US and its allies, began surging transport aircraft to the Middle East so the airlift could be stepped up massively. RAF Brize

Norton-based airlift squadrons put every available aircraft into the air to join the operation. Four C-17s, three Lockheed Martin C-130J Hercules C4/5s and four Airbus A400M Atlas C1s were committed to the operation when the airlift was at its peak. This effort was co-ordinated by the staff of 2 Group at RAF High Wycombe, under Air Vice-Marshal Al Gillespie.

US air mobility planners in the CAOC issued a daily air tasking

order to the participating air forces, allocating them landing slots at Kabul. To keep these aircraft flowing into Kabul, the USAF launched a round-the-clock support operation over Afghanistan. Each day a USAF Boeing E-3 Sentry AWACS was airborne over Kabul to choreograph the airlift.

Although the Taliban had promised not to interfere with the airlift, the US was taking no chances and throughout

the evacuation at least one Boeing B-52 Stratofortress heavy bomber and two Lockheed AC-130s gunships were always orbiting near Kabul, ready to respond to calls for help if needed.

US Navy Boeing F/A-18E/D Super Hornets from the USS *Ronald Reagan* also flew a number of 'demonstrations of force' over Kabul to show US airpower was still on hand if needed. Boeing KC-135 Stratotankers and McDonnell Douglas KC-10 Extenders were on hand in orbits near Kabul to refuel aircraft after they had left the Afghan capital. The RAF Airbus A330 Voyager KC2/3 tankers joined this effort and took their turn refuelling the US Navy jets, ensuring they had their fuel tanks topped up as they circled in Pakistani air space.

Operation Allies Refuge has been dubbed the largest humanitarian airbridge since the 1948 Berlin airlift. The crews of US and allied airlift gained well-earned credit for pushing themselves and their aircraft to the limit to bring out 124,334 people in 778 sorties out of Kabul. The British element, Operation Pitting, involved more than 100 RAF sorties into Kabul, including 46 by C-17s, 31 by A400Ms and 24 by C-130Js. On one mission 99 Squadron broke an RAF record by carrying 436 civilians on one of its C-17s, the most ever carried on an RAF aircraft. The final mission was flown on August 28.

Thirteen US military personnel were killed in a suicide bomb attack on the airport gates on August 26 but no aircraft or passengers were lost to accidents or hostile fire. An RAF C-17 missed a bus carrying civilians, that had accidentally driven onto the Kabul runway, by 10 feet, averting a potentially disastrous crash. In a matter of days, under intense pressure, US and allied air commanders pulled together a complex operation in a demanding and dynamic environment.

While those involved in the evacuation operation can be proud of their actions during August, it also marked the end of the US, UK, and NATO presence in Afghanistan. In June 1940, after the ending of the evacuation of the British Expeditionary Force from Dunkirk in northern France to England, the British Prime Minister Winston Churchill remarked, "wars are not won by evacuations".

ABOVE: RAF A330 Voyager tankers flew air refuelling missions to support the US Navy jets during the evacuation operation. (MOD/CROWN COPYRIGHT)

BELOW: US Navy F/A-18 E/F Hornets flew round-the-clock air patrols near Kabul, ready to intervene if the airport came under attack. (MOD/CROWN COPYRIGHT)

Carrier Strike Group

Britain's Fixed Wing Naval Airpower Reborn

ABOVE: Carrier power reborn. After a 10-year gap the Royal Navy is back in the aircraft carrier business. (MOD/CROWN COPYRIGHT)

For six months in 2021 the Royal Navy's flagship HMS *Queen Elizabeth* led a naval task group to the Far East and showcased the return to duty of UK fixed wing carrier-based air power.

The deployment was the culmination of the Royal Navy's project to regenerate its aircraft carrier capability after the 2010 Strategic Defence and Security Review had ordered the scrapping of the last Invincible-class carriers and their embarked Hawker Siddeley Harrier Jump Jets.

HMS *Queen Elizabeth* and the eight other ships of her task group sailed through the Mediterranean Sea, the Indian Ocean and into the Eastern Pacific region. A visit to Japan was the high point of the deployment and they conducted joint exercises with ships and aircraft of the Japanese Maritime Self-Defense Force.

The build up to the deployment of HMS *Queen Elizabeth* took several years, with the first preparations

RIGHT: Resupply at sea, including via Royal Navy Wildcat HMA2 helicopters, ensured that Carrier Strike Group 21 was able to operate far from shore bases for extended periods. (MOD/CROWN COPYRIGHT)

starting to take shape after the carrier finally took to the sea in June 2017 from Rosyth shipyard in Fife, where she was built. This was the formal start of the entry to service process of HMS *Queen Elizabeth*, which began with basic sea trials and then gradually built up to more complex evolutions involving air operations in co-ordination with large task groups of surface ships and submarines.

In the autumn of 2018, HMS *Queen Elizabeth* sailed to the United States to embark Lockheed Martin F-35B Lightning II Jump Jets for the first time. By the autumn of 2020, the carrier and her crew were ready to participate in the complex Joint Warrior exercise off the west coast of Scotland, prior to the Royal Navy declaring the ship's Initial Operating Capability, or IOC, in January 2021.

The final composition of the task group, dubbed Carrier Strike Group 2021, or CSG21, was announced at the beginning of April 2021. Providing air defence protection were two

Royal Navy Type 45 destroyers, HMS *Diamond,* and HMS *Defender.* Two British Type 23 frigates, HMS Kent and HMS Richmond provided anti-submarine protection. At-sea logistics

support was provided by the fleet tanker, RFA *Tidespring*, and solid support ship, RFA *Fort Victoria*. The Royal Navy nuclear-powered attack submarine, HMS *Astute*, accompanied CSG21 to monitor underwater threats during the task group's mission.

Multi-national participants in CSG21 included the US Navy's Arleigh Burke-class destroyer, USS *The Sullivans*, and the Royal Netherlands Navy frigate, HNLMS *Evertsen*. The USS *The Sullivans* added considerable capabilities to CSG21, including Tomahawk Land Attack cruise missiles and Standard theatre defence missiles.

The tailored air group embarked on HMS *Queen Elizabeth* included eight F-35Bs from the Royal Air Force's 617 'Dambusters' Squadron and ten F-35Bs from US Marine Fighter Attack Squadron 211 (VMFA-211), known as the 'Wake Island Avengers'. The deployment also saw

the first mission for the Crowsnest airborne early warning variant of the AgustaWestland Merlin HM2 maritime helicopters, with three being operated by 820 Naval Air Squadron. This unit also provided protection for CSG21 with its four anti-submarine Merlins. To move people and supplies around the task group, three Merlin HC4 assault helicopters of 845 Naval Air Squadron were embarked on the carrier. These helicopters had the secondary task of launching Royal Marines of 42 Commando on combat search and rescue missions to recover any F-35B pilots who might have been shot down in hostile territory or have crashed at sea.

The Type 45 destroyers and Type 23 frigates embarked four AgustaWestland Wildcat HMA2 maritime helicopters of 815 Naval Air Squadron, which were equipped with the new Thales Martlet anti-ship missile for their first operational

deployment. Additional helicopter capability was provided by an NH Industries NH90 on the Dutch ship and two Sikorsky SH-60R Seahawks on the US destroyer.

The task group was led by Royal Navy Commodore Steve Moorhouse, who had amassed plenty of experience commanding aircraft carriers, including HMS *Prince of Wales* and HMS *Ocean*. In total some 3,700 personnel, nine ships and more than 30 aircraft were under his command.

The warships and squadrons of CSG21 gathered at HM Naval Base Portsmouth in early May and then set sail for the west coast of Scotland to take part in a certification exercise to get the task group working as an integrated unit. Later in the month the task group returned to Portsmouth for final administrative activity and then set sail for the Mediterranean. »

ABOVE: Russian Naval Aviation Sukhoi Su-30SM fighter jets repeatedly buzzed HMS *Defender* during her foray into the Black Sea. (MOD/CROWN COPYRIGHT)

BELOW: HMS *Queen Elizabeth* led Carrier Strike Group 21's deployment through the Suez Canal. (MOD/CROWN COPYRIGHT)

RIGHT: HMS *Queen Elizabeth* is overflown by an RAF C-130J during exercises in the eastern Mediterranean. (MOD/CROWN COPYRIGHT)

BELOW: Royal Navy Wildcat HMA2 helicopters are being equipped with the Martlet missile to protect Carrier Strike Group 21. (LEONARDO)

Once through the Straits of Gibraltar, the carrier group conducted joint training with NATO allies in the Mediterranean before HNLMS *Evertsen* and HMS *Defender* made a foray into the Black Sea. HMS *Queen Elizabeth* remained in the Mediterranean because the international treaty covering access to the Bosporus prohibits the passage of aircraft carriers into the Black Sea. However, her aircraft were available to fly missions in support of the CSG21 warships. The two ships in the Black Sea were at the centre of an international incident after HMS *Defender* sailed through Russian-controlled waters around occupied Crimea and Russian jets repeatedly buzzed the ship at low level.

Once that phase of the deployment had been completed, the task group set sail through the Suez Canal into the Red Sea. A port visit to Al Duqm, where the UK has a Joint Logistics Support Base, then followed. The visit assessed the ability of the British base to support carriers in the Middle East and Indian Ocean region.

The next phase saw CSG21 exercise with the Indian Navy and conduct joint air operations with its carrier, INS *Vikramaditya*, as part of growing UK and US co-operation with the south Asian country.

The most sensitive part of the deployment took place en route to the Pacific, as the task force headed to Japan through the South China Sea. Tension with China over territorial disputes in that region had to be navigated delicately by the Royal Navy and the British government. London had come out strongly in support of regional allies who are in dispute with Beijing, and the UK was keen to demonstrate freedom of navigation through the South China Sea. However, the British government did not want to get into a shooting war with the Chinese People's Liberation Army Navy. In the end the passage passed without incident.

Once through the South China Sea, CSG21 was in friendlier waters off Japan and South Korea. The signing of a Maritime Security Arrangement with Japan earlier in 2021 was underpinning HMS *Queen Elizabeth*'s visit to the region, which has had long standing links to the UK stretching back to the 19th century when British shipyards built the Imperial Japanese Navy's first modern battleships.

In August, HMS *Queen Elizabeth* conducted joint exercises with the amphibious ship, USS *America,* and Japanese flat top, JS *Ise.*

After concluding its visit to the Far East, CSG21 retraced its course back home and more exercises with allied navies and port visits took place as the 20,000 nautical mile deployment

LEFT: HMS *Defender* sails in formation with the Japanese flat top, JS *Ise,* and an Oyashio-class submarine during Exercise Pacific Crown in the Philippine Sea. (MOD/CROWN COPYRIGHT)

concluded. There was a final series of exercises in the Mediterranean with the Italian Navy and this saw the loss of an RAF F-35B as it attempted to take off from HMS *Queen Elizabeth.* The incident is still under investigation but a video that was released online appears to show the aircraft suffered catastrophic engine failure on take-off. The pilot can be seen ejecting as the jet goes over the ship's ski jump and his parachute then becomes entangled in the bow of the ship. It was a remarkable escape. An international salvage operation involving the US Navy eventually recovered the wreckage

of the jet from the bottom of the Mediterranean.

For the Royal Navy, the Carrier Strike Group 2021 deployment marked the start of a new epoch in its history with its largest-ever warship proving to be fully operational and ready to project naval airpower across the globe.

No doubt the many lessons learnt during the CSG21 mission will be put to good use in future deployments but the symbolism of a British aircraft carrier being operational again will not be lost on friends and potential adversaries. The Royal Navy is well and truly back in the aircraft carrier business.

BELOW: RAF and US Marine Corps F-35Bs on the flight deck of HMS *Queen Elizabeth* as she passes through the Suez Canal. (MOD/CROWN COPYRIGHT)

Helicopters to the Rescue

Military Aid to Civilian Authorities Operations

ABOVE: Air Liaison Officers are often first on the scene at natural disasters to help co-ordinate air support. (MOD/CROWN COPYRIGHT)

When COVID-19 struck Britain in March 2020 the country was plunged into lockdown in a bid to stop the spread of the deadly virus. Normal life ground to a halt. The National Health Service went into crisis mode to cope with the huge wave of seriously ill patients.

To support this national effort the Armed Forces were put on alert to provide backup. A dedicated COVID Support Force was set up by the Ministry of Defence and it was provided with its own helicopter component.

Units from the UK's Joint Helicopter Command were placed at high readiness at four sites around the country to respond to Military Aid to Civil Authorities (MACA) tasks. These included the evacuation of COVID-19 patients or the movement of medical supplies. AgustaWestland

RIGHT: Army Air Corps Wildcat AH1 were called upon at the height of the COVID-19 pandemic to fly experts on reconnaissance missions to prepare sites for the building of the Nightingale Hospitals. (MOD/CROWN COPYRIGHT)

Wildcat AH1s from the AAC's 1 Regiment were also tasked with moving military reconnaissance teams around the country to help with the setting up of the emergency Nightingale Hospitals network.

Fixed-wing RAF transport aircraft did their part evacuating COVID-19 patients from Scottish islands and the Channel Islands to hospitals on the mainland or delivering vaccines to British Overseas Territories.

Disaster Response

The role of military aircraft in disaster relief operations in the UK has a long tradition and dates back to the 1953 storms when 12 Royal Navy Westland Dragonfly helicopters were dispatched to East Anglia in response to massive flooding. In the space of seven hours the then new naval helicopters rescued 840 people from the roofs of inundated buildings, high ground, or trees.

This century the RAF and RN helicopter crews have been in action as part of the response to many more natural disasters. In August 2004, when the Devon town of Boscastle was engulfed by a massive flash flood, seven RAF and Royal Navy Westland Sea Kings, backed by a Coast Guard Sikorsky S-61, responded to frantic calls for help from the local police. More than 100 people were on the roofs of their houses, watching cars, buildings and other debris being washed through the main street of the town by the torrent. The first two Sea Kings on the scene issued a desperate call for every available rescue helicopter in the southwest of England to be dispatched to the town to help in the rescue effort. For the next three hours the helicopters plucked 120 people from the town to safety. Miraculously no one lost their life.

These events have resulted in the UK armed forces building up a tremendous amount of experience in responding to natural disasters. Over the past two decades, the UK government and Ministry of Defence has conducted a major overhaul of disaster relief capabilities. Now the provision is known as Civil Contingencies and a special department has been set up in the Cabinet Office in Whitehall to co-ordinate both planning for events and the response once disaster has struck. This re-vamp was prompted by the 9/11 terrorist attacks in New York and Washington DC, and the structures and procedures put in place to deal with terrorist incidents are also applicable in times of natural disaster.

Military Role

The participation of UK Armed Forces in local and national emergencies, formally dubbed Military Aid to Civil Authorities or MACA, can be with either local councils, devolved governments, water and power utility companies, government bodies such as the Environment Agency, police, ambulance or fire and rescue services.

The Royal Navy, Royal Air Force and British Army have a network of regional liaison officers spread »

across the UK who maintain contact with local agencies and the emergency services. Should disaster strike, local authorities activate their emergency plans and first contact their local military liaison officer, who in turn contacts their service command. In the case of military air support – mass rescue, transport, or air surveillance – the first port of call is a network of nine RAF regional Air Liaison Officers (RALOs). They are based at RAF stations in their home region and once a request for air support has been received, they alert RAF Air Command at High Wycombe in Buckinghamshire. Staff officers at the RAF headquarters then start the process of alerting assets to be ready to deploy and at the same time they contact the Civil Contingencies Secretariat in the Cabinet Office in London to get ministerial approval for the involvement of the Armed Forces.

If a major incident is unfolding, ministers are called into the famous Cabinet Office Briefing Room, or COBR, to agree on the national response. As this is happening, the respective RALO will be on his or her way to the command centre that is co-ordinating the response to the incident. This could either be at the local police or fire headquarters, depending on the nature of the specific incident over

which command and control will be exercised. The response to major incidents that impact on a regional level often involves the activation of one of the British Army's regional brigade headquarters. These have their own air liaison staff, and, in time of crisis, they will be augmented by RAF experts from stations or Headquarters Air Command.

On Call Assets

The role of UK military airpower in MACA is in a new era. At midnight on December 31, 2015, the last military search and rescue helicopters on the UK mainland stood down after more than 60 years on duty. The RAF and RN's fleet of just over 30 SAR Sea Kings had been the first port of call at times of natural disasters. Their regional footprint meant helicopters were held on alert around the country ready to respond to calls for help.

As a result of budgetary pressures, the Ministry of Defence was unwilling to fund the purchase of a replacement for the military Sea King SAR helicopters after they were withdrawn from service in March 2016. The 2010 coalition government decided to save

even more money by outsourcing the whole of the UK SAR operation to civilian helicopters, under the umbrella of the Department for Transport's Maritime and Coastguard Agency (MCA).

The MCA's new National Maritime Operations Centre at Fareham in Hampshire became the new focus for SAR helicopters and it controls the operations of the those currently operated by the private company, Bristow Helicopters.

In this new environment, the role of military air assets in disaster relief operations in the UK has evolved considerably. The burden of support now falls on the RAF's Support Helicopter Force at RAF Benson in Oxfordshire and RAF Odiham in Hampshire, as well as the Royal Navy's Commando Helicopter Force (CHF) at Royal Naval Air Station Yeovilton in Somerset. Each of these stations has at least one helicopter on what is termed 'national standby', ready to go at a few hours' notice. They also have elements from their Mobile Air Operations Team ready to deploy around the country to co-ordinate helicopter operations. These teams are normally assigned

to army battlegroups or brigades on combat operations to help plan air support, marshal helicopters onto landing zones and connect underslung cargo. They are therefore ideal to deploy to disaster zones to

maximise the impact of military helicopters. Fortunately, the RAF Mountain Rescue Service escaped the axe when the SAR Force was disbanded and is now controlled by 85 Expeditionary Logistics Wing at RAF Wittering in Cambridgeshire.

National standby aircraft include a Boeing Chinook HC4/5/6 at RAF Odiham, a Eurocopter Puma HC2 at RAF Benson and a RN AgustaWestland Merlin HC4 under the command of the CHF at RNAS Yeovilton.

The RAF's Air Mobility Force at RAF Brize Norton in Oxfordshire also has a Lockheed Martin C-130J Hercules C4/5 and a Boeing C-17A Globemaster on national standby to move cargo or personnel in emergency situations. These aircraft can be rapidly reconfigured as air ambulances in mass casualty situations.

With climate change inducing more extreme weather events, it now seems that a major winter weather crisis can be expected every year. The UK's Civil Contingencies response capability and its air support have been put to the test with great regularity.

In the future, the UK's disaster relief organisation will find itself in action sooner than many expect. While the devotees of Hollywood disaster movies will be able to come up with unexpected scenarios, the reality of the past 20 years suggests that Britain's new civilian helicopter SAR crews, and any military helicopter personnel mobilised to augment them, need to expect the unexpected and be ready to react to whatever Mother Nature can throw at the country.

LEFT: Repairing breached dams and rivers banks has become something of a speciality for RAF Chinook crews, who have to undersling large bags of rocks to be dropped into breaches. (MOD/CROWN COPYRIGHT)

BELOW: When the COVID Support Force was set up in March 2020, RAF Puma helicopters were deployed around Britain to provide casualty evacuation and other support for civil authorities. (MOD/CROWN COPYRIGHT)

Operation Shader

RAF Patrols the Middle East

RIGHT: The British paratroopers launched from RAF Akrotiri on three C-130Js for a major exercise with the Jordanian armed forces. (MOD/CROWN COPYRIGHT)

In August 2014, RAF Lockheed Martin C130J Hercules C4/5 transport aircraft started to air drop supplies to Yazidi refugees sheltering on Mount Sinjar in northern Iraq. They had been fleeing from so-called Islamic State (IS) fighters who had surged into Iraq from Syria and were threatening to overthrow the Baghdad government to set up their so-called Caliphate. Within weeks, RAF Panavia Tornado GR4 strike jets were in action to try to turn back the advance of Jihadi fighters.

More than seven years on, the Caliphate is no more after the town of Baghuz in southeastern Syria was captured by Kurdish fighters backed by US and British special forces and airpower in March 2019. Thousands of IS fighters were captured in the fall of Baghuz but many more escaped and tried to hide in the desert region astride the Syrian/Iraqi border.

BELOW: Defence engagement with friendly nations across the Middle East, such as Qatar, is regularly conducted by RAF Typhoons to boost defence co-operation and exports. (MOD/CROWN COPYRIGHT)

The end of the physical Caliphate was not the end of IS. Its surviving fighters resorted to guerrilla tactics, staging hit-and-run raids on Syrian, Kurdish, and Iraqi military outposts in a bid to destabilise the region.

The US and its allies in the counter-IS coalition, Operation Inherent Resolve, took the opportunity to scale down their forces in the Middle East, but there was a recognition that a residual capability was needed in the region to prevent a resurgence of the Caliphate. Britain's contribution to the reduced coalition – Operation Shader – was centred on airpower and a small contingent of Special Forces on the ground.

provided by Airbus A330 Voyager KC2/3s also based in Cyprus. A launch and recovery element for RAF General Atomics MQ-9 Reaper unmanned aerial vehicles remains at Ali Al Salem Air Base in Kuwait. The combat phase of RAF UAV missions across the Middle East is controlled via satellite from command centres at RAF Waddington in Lincolnshire and Creech Air Force Base in Nevada.

To provide support to the remaining British troops in Syria and Iraq, a C-130J is usually based in Cyprus. The UK air component in the Middle East is also tasked with supporting the Royal Navy presence in the Arabian Gulf, under the banner of Operation Kipion, »

LEFT: A330 Voyager tankers support all Operation Shader Typhoon missions from RAF Akrotiri in Cyprus. (MOD/CROWN COPYRIGHT)

Controlling the UK air element of Operation Shader is the 83 Expeditionary Air Group (EAG) at Al Udeid Air Base in Qatar, under the command of an RAF Air Commodore. His staff work inside the US-run Combined Air Operations Centre or CAOC, which co-ordinates all coalition air missions across the Middle East.

The main RAF elements committed to Operation Shader are currently based at RAF Akrotiri in Cyprus. Each of the RAF's Eurofighter Typhoon FGR4 squadrons has spent four months at a time at RAF Akrotiri on Operation Shader duty. Air-to-air refuelling support is

LEFT: Friendly nation's aircraft are often refuelled during Operation Shader missions over Iraq and Syria from RAF Voyager tankers. (MOD/CROWN COPYRIGHT)

with air movement elements in Bahrain and in the United Arab Emirates. The 903rd Expeditionary Air Wing at Minhad Air Base in the UAE acts as an air transport hub in the Gulf region. In addition, the 83rd EAG coordinates support for UK exercises and defence engagement with allies across the Middle East.

The fast jets of the Operation Shader Typhoon Detachment are tasked with flying daily missions into the operational area, ready to respond to calls for assistance from UK or coalition ground troops. Air planners organise a rotation of fast

jets and armed UAVs over Iraq and Syria on a daily basis, so air assets are always on station.

Typically, a pair of Typhoons are launched from RAF Akrotiri, accompanied by a Voyager tanker, and they transit over Israel and Jordan before taking their place on a combat air patrol station over western Iraq or eastern Syria. Once on station, the Typhoons are usually tasked with conducting air-to-ground coordination training with coalition forward air controllers. If coalition troops come under threat or attack, then the jets can be released to either fly shows of force over crisis zones

or actually drop weapons in close air support strikes.

In January 2022, the Typhoons were called in to help Kurdish fighters, US and UK Special Forces trying to contain a riot by 3,000 IS prisoners held in a prison in the Geweran district of Al Hasakah in northeastern Syria. The fanatical prisoners overpowered guards and seized their weapons. Several air strikes by coalition aircraft eventually helped Kurdish fighters contain the riot.

Coalition intelligence is continuously tracking IS fighters and when their hideouts are discovered

In a notable attack in March 2021, three Typhoons used the MBDA Storm Shadow long range cruise missile in action for the first time to hit a network of caves in northern Iraq.

In December 2021, a Typhoon conducted the first air-to-air engagement by an RAF aircraft since the Korean War in the 1950s. An RAF Typhoon was called to engage a small drone operating in a threatening manner near the US base at Al Tanf on the Syrian/Jordan border. The pilot fired a single MBDA Advanced Short Range Air-to-Air Missile (ASRAAM) that destroyed the drone and made history.

June 2021 also saw history being made when RAF Lockheed Martin F-35B Lightning II Jump Jets launched off the carrier HMS *Queen Elizabeth* and flew combat air patrols over Syria and Iraq. This marked the first time in over a decade that British fast jets had flown a combat mission off a Royal Navy aircraft carrier.

LEFT: Paratroopers from 16 Air Assault Brigade were dropped into the Jordanian desert by RAF C-130J. (MOD/CROWN COPYRIGHT)

BELOW: Typhoons are still on duty at RAF Akrotiri in Cyprus to fly missions against the remnants of IS across Syria and Iraq. (MOD/CROWN COPYRIGHT)

Special Forces raids are organised to sweep the locations, backed by pre-planned air strikes.

Over the last year the RAF Typhoons and Reapers have been in action on 13 occasions, flying a mix of close air support and pre-planned missions. Typhoon strikes usually involve Paveway II laser/GPS guided weapons and the Reapers regularly use their Hellfire missiles.

As well as being very long missions, with pilots often spending more than six hours in their cockpits, the airspace over Syria is highly congested with coalition, Syrian, Russian, Israeli, and Turkish aircraft all operating on a daily basis. This requires constant coordination with mission controllers in the CAOC or on Boeing E-3 Sentry AWACS aircraft to ensure all the aircraft remain safely deconflicted.

Royal Air Force in 2022

RIGHT: British airpower over the White Cliffs of Dover. The Typhoon Display Team shows off its 2021 colour scheme at an iconic location. (MOD/CROWN COPYRIGHT)

As the world's first-ever independent air arm, the Royal Air Force has led the way in many aspects of air warfare. Radar air defence networks gave the RAF the edge against Hitler's Luftwaffe in 1940 and later in World War Two, Bomber Command fielded the first combat effective four-engine heavy bombers. In the 1950s RAF pilots flew some of the first supersonic fighter jets.

In the third decade of the 21st century the RAF is still striving to remain in the first division of air forces by fielding the most advanced air warfare technology and leading the world in combat tactics and procedures.

BELOW: Air-to-air refuelling is central to many RAF operations. (MOD/CROWN COPYRIGHT)

Fast Jet Force

After the delivery of the first Lockheed Martin F-35B Lightning IIs to RAF Marham in Norfolk in 2018, the RAF has been steadily learning how to exploit the potential of its first combat aircraft, incorporating low observable technology. By early 2022, the RAF had taken delivery of 27 F-35Bs and some 21 more are under contract to be delivered by 2025. One was lost in an accident off HMS *Queen Elizabeth* in the Mediterranean in 2021.

The seven frontline squadrons equipped with the Eurofighter Typhoon FGR4 have been kept busy taking over many roles previously filled by the Panavia Tornado GR4, after the classic jet retired from service in 2019. At the same time, the Typhoon force has sustained quick reaction alert (QRA) commitments in the UK and the Falkland Islands. Typhoon also routinely fills NATO Air Policing tasks in Eastern Europe, as well as supporting Operation Shader from RAF Akrotiri in Cyprus.

Eyes in the Sky

The RAF intelligence, surveillance, target acquisition and reconnaissance (ISTAR) force remains highly active

LEFT: The A400M Atlas airlifter is now a familiar sight across the UK and around the world. (MOD/CROWN COPYRIGHT)

in support of Operation Shader in the Middle East as well as around Europe supporting NATO allies. Outside of the US, the UK has some of the most flexible and effective ISTAR platforms available, so they are much in demand by operational commanders.

Boeing RC-135 Rivet Joint electronic intelligence-gathering aircraft have been regular visitors to Middle Eastern and East European skies over the past year. Beechcraft Shadow R1 multi-sensor ISTAR aircraft have also been reported operating in Northern Iraq and Eastern Syria, as well as at home on counter-terrorist tasks. A launch and recovery element for the RAF General Atomics MQ-9 Reaper unmanned aerial vehicles remains at Ali al Salem Air Base in Kuwait, while the aircraft are controlled remotely from RAF Waddington in the UK and Creech AFB in Nevada while on station.

A major boost for the RAF ISTAR Force was the delivery of the first Boeing Poseidon MRA1 to RAF Kinloss in Moray in February 2020, and the full fleet of nine aircraft has now taken up permanent residence at its home base at RAF Lossiemouth.

Planned future additions to the RAF ISTAR Force include the Boeing Wedgetail AEW1 airborne early warning aircraft from December 2023 and the new General Atomics Protector RG1 UAV from 2024.

However, it has emerged that to find the money to buy this new equipment the RAF has had to retire existing capabilities. All the Raytheon Sentinel R1 aircraft were retired in March 2021 without

replacement and the Boeing E-3D Sentry airborne early warning radar aircraft flew their last operational sorties in September 2021, leaving a gap of at least two years during which the RAF will have no airborne early warning capability.

Air Transport and Helicopters

The Air Transport Force at RAF Brize Norton remains one of the busiest elements in the RAF, sustaining Air Force, Navy and Army units deployed around the world. It has benefited from procurement programmes over the past two decades that have seen the Airbus A330 Voyager KC2/3,

Boeing C-17A Globemaster and Airbus A400M Atlas C1 come into service and older aircraft retire.

The defence review in March 2021 ordered the retirement of the Lockheed Martin C-130J Hercules C4/5 fleet.

It emerged in late 2019 that the Ministry of Defence is to sell off the four BAe 146s used by 32 (The Royal) Squadron at RAF Northolt for VIP and command support operations. The French-made Dassault 900LX was selected in February 2022 as the replacement.

The RAF support helicopters, Boeing Chinook HC4/5/6s and Eurocopter Puma HC2s, remain »

BELOW: RAF Chinooks have a key role in supporting the British Army and Special Forces on exercises and operations around the world. (MOD/CROWN COPYRIGHT)

RIGHT: The Typhoon is at the heart of the RAF's fast jet fighter force. (MOD/CROWN COPYRIGHT)

BELOW: The RC-135 Rivet Joint is the RAF's 'big ear', listening into the radio and mobile telephone communications in hostile states. (MOD/CROWN COPYRIGHT)

under the command of the tri-service Joint Helicopter Command.

Flooding around Britain has seen the Chinook Force called upon on several occasions to help reinforce flood defences and build up faltering dams. Since July 2018, the Chinook Force has also sustained a detachment of three helicopters in Mali in North Africa, supporting French troops fighting militants. This on top of an enduring mission in the Middle East to support UK Special Forces across the region from RAF Akrotiri on Cyprus.

Training Fleet Boost

In early 2019, the RAF-led Military Flying Training System (MFTS) came in for serious criticism from the media, parliamentarians, and the spending watchdogs at the National Audit Office for the large number of pilots and aircrew 'on hold' or waiting to complete their training.

The then new Defence Secretary, Ben Wallace, revealed that the RAF alone was suffering from a shortage of 250 pilots as a result of problems in the MFTS. These stemmed from the Ministry of Defence not funding the extra capacity in MFTS needed to train personnel to fly the extra

Poseidons and Protector RG1s ordered in the 2015 defence review and for the formation of additional Typhoon squadrons.

At the same time, many of the new training aircraft, helicopters and simulators ordered to recapitalise the RAF No 22 Group's legacy equipment had not yet been delivered. To try to turn around this situation, No 22 Group instigated mitigation measures to reduce the backlog in the training pipeline. Fast jet and helicopter students were sent to train with the US Air Force and US Army, while multi-engine pilots have been training with civilian flight academies in the UK.

The final piece in the MFTS recapitalisation project occurred in 2019 when the last Shorts Tucano T1 course was run at RAF Linton-upon-Ouse in Yorkshire and the first students started training on the Beechcraft Texan T1 at RAF Valley in Anglesey. The final Tucano flights took place in October 2019, just as the first Texan course got underway at the Welsh base.

To increase the capacity of the Defence Helicopter Flying School at RAF Shawbury in Shropshire, four more Airbus H145 Jupiter HT1s were ordered in January 2020.

RAF Future

The UK government's Integrated Review of Security, Defence, Development and Foreign Policy requirements published in March 2021 put many of the RAF programmes under intense scrutiny as it looked to turn ambitions for Global Britain into reality. Although it is early days, the central role of the Royal Navy's aircraft carriers means that maritime airpower will be at the heart of the future RAF, with the Poseidons having an important role protecting UK carrier battlegroups from hostile submarines.

The purchase of 138 F-35Bs looks like it will not happen because of the costs involved, and the future of the RAF's Combat Air capability seems to be resting with the Tempest project. BAE Systems and a consortium of British companies are working on a demonstrator project and a future combat aircraft has to be ready to replace the Typhoon at the end of the next decade. The new aircraft is expected to be designed to fight as part of a constellation of manned and unmanned aircraft.

The RAF has also taken the lead in military space operations, with senior officers leading efforts to direct Britain's role in coordinating current and future activity in space. This includes the replacement of the UK's existing constellation of communications satellites and moving to acquire new space-based intelligence gathering systems.

The potential for so-called 'near space' planes to transform air warfare is recognised by the RAF and other air arms around the world. Once in service they could have global reach and operate beyond the range of existing air defence systems. The sky is truly no longer the limit for the RAF in the 21st century.

Royal Air Force Order of Battle

Royal Air Force Flying Units, April 2022			
Unit	**Aircraft Type**	**Role**	**Location**
RAF Air Command			RAF High Wycombe
Air Warfare Centre			RAF Waddington
41 Squadron	Typhoon FGR4/T3	Fast Jet Test & Evaluation Squadron	RAF Coningsby
56 Squadron	Poseidon MRA1, RC-135, Shadow R1	Operational Test & Evaluation Unit	RAF Waddington
206 Squadron	Hercules C4/C5, C-17, Voyager KC2/KC3, A400M Atlas C1	Operational Test & Evaluation Unit	QinetiQ Boscombe Down, Wiltshire
17 Squadron	F-38B Lightning	Operational Test & Evaluation Unit	Edwards Air Force Base, California, USA
Headquarters No 1 Group			RAF High Wycombe
Battle Britain Memorial Flight	Spitfire, Hurricane, Lancaster, Dakota, Chipmunk	Flying Displays	RAF Coningsby
Joint Forward Air Control Training Standards Unit	Hawk T1	FAC/Dissimilar Air Combat/Advanced Fast Jet Training	RAF Leeming
RAF Aerobatic Team	Hawk T1	Flying Displays	RAF Scampton
Headquarters Typhoon Force			RAF Coningsby
1 (Fighter) Squadron	Typhoon FGR4	Multi-Role Unit	RAF Lossiemouth
II (AC) Squadron	Typhoon FGR4	Multi-Role Unit	RAF Lossiemouth
3 (Fighter) Squadron	Typhoon FGR4	QRA/Lead Air Defence Squadron	RAF Coningsby
6 Squadron	Typhoon FGR4	QRA/Air-to-Air Squadron	RAF Lossiemouth
XI Squadron	Typhoon FGR4	Lead Air-to-Ground Squadron	RAF Coningsby
12 (Bomber) Squadron	Typhoon FGR4	Multi-Role Unit/ Qatari Training Unit	RAF Coningsby
IX Squadron	Typhoon FGR4	Multi-Role/ Aggressor Unit	RAF Lossiemouth
29 Squadron	Typhoon FGR4/T3	Typhoon Operational Conversion Unit	RAF Coningsby
Headquarters Lightning Force			RAF Marham
207 Squadron	F-38B Lightning II	F-35B Operational Conversion Unit	RAF Marham
617 Squadron	F-38B Lightning II	Strike/CV Squadrons	RAF Marham
809 Naval Air Squadron	F-38B Lightning II	To be formed in 2023/4?	RAF Marham
Headquarters ISTAR Force			RAF Waddington
13 Squadron	MQ-9 Reaper	Strike/ISTAR (to convert to Protector RG1 in 2023)	RAF Waddington
14 Squadron	Shadow R1	Tactical ISTAR	RAF Waddington
31 Squadron	Protector RG1	Strike/ISTAR (from 2023)	RAF Waddington
39 Squadron	MQ-9 Reaper	Strike/ISTAR	Creech AFB, USA
51 Squadron	RC-135 Rivet Joint	SIGINT/COMINT	RAF Waddington/ Offutt AFB, Nebraska, USA
54 Squadron	Poseidon MRA1, RC-135, Shadow R1	ISTAR Operational Conversion Unit	RAF Waddington
Reaper Formal Training Unit	MQ-9 Reaper	UAV Operational Conversion Unit	Holloman AFB, New Mexico, USA
120 Squadron	Poseidon MRA1	Maritime Patrol	RAF Lossiemouth
201 Squadron	Poseidon MRA1	Maritime Patrol	RAF Lossiemouth
P-8 Flight, 54 Squadron	Poseidon MRA1	P-8A Operational Conversion Unit	RAF Lossiemouth
Headquarters No 2 Group			RAF High Wycombe
Headquarters AT/ AAR Force			RAF Brize Norton
10 Squadron	Voyager KC2/KC3	Air-to-Air Refuelling/ Strategic Air Transport	RAF Brize Norton
24 Squadron	Hercules C4/C5, A400M Atlas C1	Operational Conversion Unit	RAF Brize Norton
30 Squadron	A400M Atlas C1	Tactical Air Transport	RAF Brize Norton
32 (The Royal) Squadron	Dassault 900LX, A109SP	VIP/ Communications	RAF Northolt
47 Squadron	C-130J Hercules C4/C5	Tactical Air Transport/SF Support	RAF Brize Norton
70 Squadron	A400M Atlas C1	Tactical Air Transport	RAF Brize Norton
99 Squadron	C-17A Globemaster III	Strategic Air Transport	RAF Brize Norton
101 Squadron	Voyager KC2/KC3	Air-to-Air Refuelling/ Strategic Air Transport	RAF Brize Norton

BELOW LEFT: Typhoon squadrons take turns to deploy to RAF Akrotiri in Cyprus for Operation Shader duty.
(MOD/CROWN COPYRIGHT)

BELOW RIGHT: RAF Brize Norton is the RAF's main hub for global airlift and air-to-air refuelling operations.
(MOD/CROWN COPYRIGHT)

Headquarters No 22 Group

Unit	Aircraft	Role	Base
IV (Army Co-operation) Squadron	Hawk T2	Advanced Jet Training	RAF Valley
11 Squadron (Qatar)	Hawk Mk 167	Advanced Jet Training for Qatari Air Force	RAF Leeming
16 Squadron	Grob G 115E Tutor T1	Fixed Wing Elementary Training	RAF Wittering
25 (Fighter) Squadron	Hawk T2	Advanced Jet Training	RAF Valley
45 Squadron	Embraer Phenom T1	Multi-engine Training	RAF Cranwell
57 Squadron	Grob 120TP Prefect T1	Fixed Wing Elementary Training	RAF Cranwell
60 Squadron	H135 Juno HT1	Basic Rotary Wing Training (DHFS)	RAF Shawbury
72 Squadron	T-6C Texan T1	Basic Fast Jet Training	RAF Valley
115 Squadron	Grob G 115E Tutor T1	Instructor Training	RAF Wittering
202 Squadron	H145 Jupiter HT1/H135 Juno HT1	Basic SAR Training	RAF Valley
University Air Squadrons	Grob G 115E Tutor T1	Air Experience	various
ATC Air Experience Flights	Grob G 115E Tutor T1	Air Experience	various
Volunteer Gliding Squadrons	Viking T1	Air Experience	various

Army Headquarters/Joint Helicopter Command — Andover

Unit	Aircraft	Role	Base
18 (Bomber) Squadron	Chinook HC4/5/6	Support Helicopter	RAF Odiham
22 Squadron	Chinook HC4/5/6, Puma HC2	JHC Operational Evaluation Unit	RAF Benson
27 Squadron	Chinook HC4/5/6	Support Helicopter	RAF Odiham
28 (Army Co-operation) Squadron	Chinook HC4/5/6, Puma HC2	Operational Conversion Unit	RAF Benson
33 Squadron	Puma HC2	Support Helicopter	RAF Benson
230 Squadron	Puma HC2	Support Helicopter	RAF Benson

Directorate of Special Forces/Joint Special Forces Aviation Wing

Unit	Aircraft	Role	Base
7 Squadron	Chinook HC4/5/6	Support Helicopter/ SF Support	RAF Odiham

Permanent Joint Headquarters

Unit	Aircraft	Role	Base
HQ British Forces Falkland Islands			RAF Mount Pleasant, Falklands
1435 Flight	Typhoon FGR4	QRA/Air Defence	RAF Mount Pleasant, Falklands
1312 Flight	Hercules C4/C5, Voyager KC2/KC3	Tactical Transport/ MPA/AAR	RAF Mount Pleasant, Falklands

HQ British Forces Cyprus

Unit	Aircraft	Role	Base
84 Squadron	Griffin HAR2	Search and Rescue (Resident Unit)	RAF Akrotiri, Cyprus

Royal Air Force Inventory, April 2022

	Total
Fixed-wing Platforms	
A400M Atlas C1	20
RC-135 Rivet Joint	3
C-17A Globemaster	8
Hawk T1/T1A	67
Hawk T2	28
C130J Hercules C4/C5	14
Phenom T1	5
Poseidon MRA1	9
Prefect T1	23
F-35B Lightning II	26
Shadow R1	8
Texan T1	10
Tutor T1	91
Typhoon FGR4	137
Viking T1	81
A330 Voyager KC2/KC3	9
Dassault 900LX	2
Unmanned Aircraft Systems	
MQ-9 Reaper	10
Rotary-wing Platforms	
AW109SP	1
Chinook HC4/5/6/6A	60
Griffin HAR2	3
Juno HT1	29
Jupiter HT1	7
Puma HC2	23

Source: UK Armed Forces Equipment and Formations annual report by UK Ministry of Defence

LEFT: The RAF's maritime patrol capability is being re-build with the delivery of Boeing Poseidon MRA1 aircraft.
(MOD/CROWN COPYRIGHT)

LEFT: RAF Benson's Puma HC2 medium helicopters continue to give stalwart service.
(MOD/CROWN COPYRIGHT)

BELOW: 51 Squadron's RC-135 Rivet Joint signals intelligence gathering aircraft operate around the world in close cooperation with its USAF counterparts.
(MOD/CROWN COPYRIGHT)

Royal Air Force Groups and Stations in 2022

Airpower Profile

RIGHT: Multi-role Typhoon aircraft are at the heart of the RAF air combat force.
(MOD/CROWN COPYRIGHT)

The Royal Air Force continues to evolve to meet new threats and demanding targets from the government to improve its efficiency. Operating modern military aircraft is an expensive business and over the past decade the RAF has had to consolidate by reducing its fleet into a smaller number of bases.

Frontline Force – No 1 Group

No 1 Group is responsible for all of the service's frontline, fast-jet force elements and the Intelligence Surveillance, Target Acquisition and Reconnaissance (ISTAR) work.

In 2022 it had 8,500 personnel who worked from four main operating bases and several smaller sites. The group is headquartered at RAF High

BELOW: Quick Reaction Alert Typhoons are routinely scrambled to intercept Russian aircraft operating in the UK Flight Information Region.
(MOD/CROWN COPYRIGHT)

Wycombe in Buckinghamshire and its flying squadrons – or as they are known in RAF jargon, force elements at readiness – are controlled by force headquarters for their respective aircraft type or specific mission. No 1 Group has no day-to-day operational control of its units or aircraft but is what is termed a force generation organisation.

The Air Officer Commanding No 1 Group is responsible for ensuring that his aircraft and people are ready to deploy on operations at the required time. To ensure this No 1 Group's squadrons operate according to a readiness cycle that sees them first take part in training exercises and then be held at readiness or alert to deploy on operations or overseas missions, such as Operation Shader in the Middle East or NATO Air Policing in eastern Europe.

A major commitment for No 1 Group is to support the aircraft, aircrew and ground support personnel to sustain the 24/7 Typhoon Quick Reaction Alert (QRA) detachments in the UK and the Falkland Islands. Once on duty, however, the QRA detachments report to the National Air & Space Operations Centre (NASOC) at RAF High Wycombe and the Headquarters British Forces South Atlantic Islands at the Mount Pleasant Complex on East Falkland, respectively.

By far the biggest organisation within No 1 Group is the Typhoon Force and it currently controls seven frontline squadrons equipped with the Eurofighter Typhoon FGR4 combat aircraft, as well as the operational conversion unit.

The Typhoon Force is split between RAF Coningsby in Lincolnshire and RAF Lossiemouth in Moray. Each station houses an active QRA site, with a pair of Typhoons held at high readiness to launch within minutes of receiving a command from the NASOC. Each squadron at these stations takes a turn to stand up the QRA detachment, providing pilots and ground personnel for 24 hour shifts, every day of the year. The QRA sites are secure locations, protected by the RAF Police to ensure there is no interruption to any scramble commands.

The aircraft and personnel assigned to QRA duty were significantly expanded after the 9/11 attacks on New York and Washington in 2001. Then the main threat was seen as terrorist hijacking of airliners and the decision was taken to run two QRA sites simultaneously. Additional temporary QRA sites were also designed in the south of England to allow a rapid expansion of fighter coverage in a time of enhanced threat. During the 2012 Olympic Games, Typhoons were forward based at RAF Northolt in northeast

London to provide a rapid response capability. Once or twice a year the RAF Coningsby QRA aircraft are scrambled to intercept airliners that are suspected of posing a terrorist threat. Invariably these turn out to be just a case of communication problems.

Since 2014 the threat from incursions into the UK air traffic control or Flight Information Region (FIR) by large Russian aircraft, Tupolev Tu-95 Bears and Tu-160 Blackjacks flying down into the North Atlantic and North Sea, has increased. These Cold War-era bombers routinely do not have their navigation transponders on, so they present a hazard to civilian aircraft, requiring the launching of Typhoons to investigate.

The headquarters of the Typhoon Force is at RAF Coningsby in Lincolnshire. It is co-located with the Typhoon operational conversion unit, 29 Squadron, and the Typhoon depth maintenance facility where all the RAF's Typhoons are overhauled. There are two frontline squadrons, 3 (Fighter) and XI (Fighter), and a third unit, 12 (Bomber) Squadron, which is a joint UK/Qatari unit that will be training up the Gulf state's Typhoon unit from 2022.

RAF Coningsby also plays host to the Battle of Britain Memorial Flight, with its iconic Avro Lancaster, Supermarine Spitfire, Hawker ❯❯

BELOW: A Typhoon launches from RAF Coningsby in Lincolnshire, which is the home of the RAF Typhoon Force. (MOD/CROWN COPYRIGHT)

Hurricane and Douglas Dakota aircraft that date from World War Two. Apart from a small cadre of permanent staff, the BBMF draws on many volunteers from across the station to keep the RAF's link to its past in the air.

At RAF Lossiemouth, 1 (Fighter) Squadron, No II (Army Co-operation) Squadron and 6 Squadron operate the Typhoon FGR4. As a result of the 2015 defence review the station received an additional Typhoon unit, IX (Bomber) Squadron, equipped with the Tranche 1 variant of the aircraft. These are the older aircraft that do not have the full multi-role capabilities of the Tranche 2 and 3 Typhoons, so they are used primarily for QRA duties and in the aggressor role to train other squadrons. The 2021 defence review, however, said that the Tranche 1 Typhoons should be retired by 2025 so it would seem that IX (Bomber) Squadron is set to be disbanded, although official confirmation has yet to be made.

The Typhoon Force remains one of the busiest parts of the RAF. As well as sustaining the two QRA detachments in the UK it has to provide aircraft and personnel for 1435 Flight in the Falkland Islands. Since 2015, Typhoon squadrons have taken turns to provide a permanent presence at RAF Akrotiri in Cyprus in the eastern Mediterranean to

support Operation Shader. On top of this, each year at least one Typhoon squadron heads to eastern Europe for a four-month long stint doing NATO Air Policing in either the Baltic or Black Sea regions.

In between these standing commitments, a Typhoon squadron is regularly deployed to Oman for Exercise Magic Carpet and Exercise Red Flag in the United States.

The final element of the Typhoon Force is the operational test and evaluation unit, 41 Squadron. This unit has the job of accepting all new equipment into service on the Typhoon. Although located at RAF Coningsby, 41 Squadron reports to the Air Warfare Centre at RAF Waddington in Lincolnshire. It works

closely with the manufacturer of the UK's Typhoons, BAE Systems, and also routinely deploys to test ranges in the USA and Sweden to live fire new weapons.

The newest fast jet to enter RAF service is the Lockheed Martin F-35B Lightning II Jump Jet, which is based at RAF Marham in Norfolk under the control of Lightning Force (LF). Currently there is one operational F-35B unit, the famous 617 'Dambusters' Squadron and an operational conversion unit, 207 Squadron.

The primary task of the LF is to generate aircraft, aircrew, and ground support personnel to provide the air group for the two Queen Elizabeth-class aircraft carriers. So,

both RAF and Royal Navy personnel serve in the LF and, from 2023, in a second operational unit, 809 Naval Air Squadron (NAS). The training and operations of the LF are closely synchronised with the sailing programme of the aircraft carriers and it is now routine for 617 Squadron to deploy for at least one extended cruise on one of the carriers each year.

A major focus is on generating aircrew who have the necessary qualifications to fly off aircraft carriers, so each year student pilots from 207 Squadron undertake short deployments on board one of the carriers cruising in UK waters.

The intention is that the RAF will take delivery of all 48 of its initial batch of F-35Bs by 2025 and this is leading to an increase in training to build up enough instructors and student pilots to allow 809 NAS to stand up. The plan had been to form 809 NAS in April 2023 but this may now slip, and there will also be a delay in building its dedicated facilities at RAF Marham.

The final element of the LF is 17 Squadron, which is based at Edwards Air Force Base in California and is the UK's contribution to the US-led F-35 testing task force.

The RAF's Intelligence, Surveillance, Target Acquisition and Reconnaissance (ISTAR) force is split between two stations, RAF Waddington, and RAF Lossiemouth. The Lincolnshire station became the focus for ISTAR in the 1990s when the Boeing E-3D Sentry AWACS and Hawker Siddeley Nimrod R1 signals intelligence aircraft moved there.

More ISTAR aircraft followed in the 21st century, including the Raytheon Sentinel R1 Airborne Stand-off Radar (ASTOR) jets, Beechcraft Shadow R1 counter-terrorist intelligence gathering aircraft and the control hubs for the General Atomics MQ-9 Reaper unmanned aerial vehicles. From 2013 the first Boeing RC-135 Rivet Joint signals intelligence gathering aircraft arrived to fill the gap left by the retirement of the Nimrod R1s in 2011.

RAF Waddington is also home to 1 Intelligence, Surveillance, and Reconnaissance Wing, which specialises in analysing and exploiting intelligence products collected from a variety of sources.

Over the past year, RAF Waddington has been losing aircraft with the retirement of the E-3Ds of 8 Squadron and the Sentinel R1s of V (Army Co-operation) Squadron. This has made space for the building of new operating facilities for the Protector RG1 unmanned aerial vehicles and an expansion of the Shadow R1 unit, 14 Squadron. RAF Waddington is soon to become the home of the famous RAF Aerobatic Team, the Red Arrows, after it moves from its current base at the historic RAF Scampton when it closes.

The RAF has ambitions to transform RAF Waddington into the 'Nellis of Europe' and build it up as a centre of excellence for training and experimentation. It is home to the Air Warfare Centre, which is leading this drive. Already 216 Squadron has reformed at the station to experiment with so-called swarming UAVs. »

ABOVE: 617 Squadron is now routinely participating in exercises around the world with its F-35B Lightning IIs. (MOD/CROWN COPYRIGHT)

BELOW: Nine Poseidon MRA1 maritime patrol aircraft are now based at RAF Lossiemouth in Moray to monitor naval activity across the North Atlantic. (MOD/CROWN COPYRIGHT)

No 1 Group's newest component is the Boeing Poseidon MRA1 fleet based at RAF Lossiemouth. It is in the process of re-establishing the RAF maritime patrol capability that was lost when the BAE Systems Nimrod MRA4 was scrapped in 2010. It has two flying units, 120 and 201 Squadrons. RAF Lossiemouth has also been designated at the home of the new Boeing Wedgetail AEW1 airborne early warning and control aircraft when they enter service from 2023.

The final No 1 Group station is RAF Leeming in North Yorkshire, which was home to 100 Squadron with its black painted Hawker Siddeley Hawk T1A jets. They had been providing dissimilar air combat training for RAF and allied fighter units, as well as supporting the RAF Leeming-based Joint Forward Air Controller Training and Standards Unit. As a cost-saving measure, the RAF decided to take the Hawk T1/

T1A out of service on March 31, 2022. The intention is to replace them with a contractor-operated service using Aero L-159E Honey Badgers operated by Draken International.

Airlift and Support – No 2 Group

The RAF has now grouped all its air and ground-based support elements and units under the command of No 2 Group, which is headquartered at RAF High Wycombe in Buckinghamshire.

Its most prominent element is the Air Mobility Force at RAF Brize Norton in Oxfordshire. The air transport and air-to-air refuelling fleets have gone through a process of recapitalisation with the new Airbus A330 Voyager KC2/3 and the A400M Atlas C1 joining the stalwart Boeing C-17A Globemaster and Lockheed Martin C-130J Hercules C4/5. New facilities have been built for the new aircraft as part of a major

redevelopment of the Oxfordshire station.

The pattern of UK air transport and air-to-air refuelling operations has changed as a result of the scaling down of operations in the Middle East. British troops had to withdraw from Afghanistan in August 2021 and only a small number of counter-terrorist and training personnel remain in Iraq. These troops are supported by C130Js based at RAF Akrotiri in Cyprus and by A400Ms based at Minhad Air Base in the United Arab Emirates. A Voyager is also based at RAF Akrotiri to provide refuelling support to the Typhoons participating in Operation Shader.

A single Voyager and an A400M are based at Mount Pleasant airport on the Falklands to support the defence of Britain's South Atlantic islands.

The remainder of the Air Mobility Force is home based at RAF Brize Norton and is held at readiness to support operations or exercises.

BELOW: 51 Squadron from RAF Waddington in Lincolnshire operate the RC-135 Rivet Joint.
(MOD/CROWN COPYRIGHT)

The C-17 unit, 99 Squadron, flies any strategic missions that require outsized cargoes to be moved around the world.

10 and 101 Squadrons are the core of the Air Tanker fleet that provides strategic air transport and air-to-air refuelling under a service agreement with a civilian consortium, as well VIP transport with a specially configured Voyager for government ministers and members of the royal family.

The A400M is operated by 30 and 70 Squadrons in both strategic air transport and tactical roles. It is progressively being cleared to take on a tactical parachuting role, dropping paratroopers and cargo, which will eventually allow it to replace the C-130J.

Only one unit, 47 Squadron, continues to operate the highly versatile C-130J in support of the British Army's 16 Air Assault Brigade and a variety of Special Forces units. For financial reasons, the Ministry of Defence has decided to withdraw the C-130J to save £289m, almost exactly the amount being spent building the National Flagship which is intended to replace the old Royal Yacht *Britannia*.

A C-130J is usually forward based at RAF Akrotiri to support Special Forces missions in the Middle East, while others are held at high readiness at Brize Norton to support short-notice operations or exercises.

Operational conversion for all C-17, Voyager, A400M and C-130J crews is conducted at RAF Brize Norton »

ABOVE: The veteran C-130J Hercules' outstanding performance allows it to get in and out of battlefield air strips. (MOD/CROWN COPYRIGHT)

BELOW: Global mobility is the name of the game for the C-17 Globemasters of 99 Squadron. Here one is unloading a Chinook heavy lift helicopter. (MOD/CROWN COPYRIGHT)

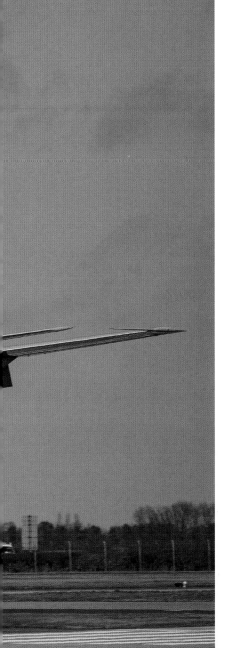

ABOVE: The A400M Atlas is now coming on line with No 2 Group, flying both strategic and tactical airlift roles. (MOD/CROWN COPYRIGHT)

BELOW: The Air Tanker Consortium provides the A330 Voyager aircraft to the RAF under a private finance arrangement. (MOD/CROWN COPYRIGHT)

by the Air Mobility Operational Conversion Unit, 206 Squadron. This includes all training from basic flying skills through to tactical operations, including landings on improvised airstrips which are practiced at Pendine Sands in south Wales. New equipment and tactics on RAF air transport aircraft are tested by 206 Squadron and the Joint Air Delivery Test and Evaluation Unit is responsible for approving new parachuting and helicopter cargo movement procedures.

RAF Brize Norton is the home of British military parachuting and since 1976 has been the home of the UK's parachute training school. It is currently under the umbrella of the Airborne Delivery Wing. Every year hundreds of personnel from the Royal Navy, Royal Marines and RAF undergo basic parachute training at the Wing, which is also responsible for the packing and repair of all UK military parachutes.

The RAF is in charge of the safe air movement of members of the royal

RAF Force Protection Units in 2022
RAF Honington, Suffolk
RAF Force Protection Headquarters
Specialist Police Wing/3 Tactical Police Squadron
RAF Leeming, North Yorkshire
No 2 Force Protection Wing
34 Squadron, RAF Regiment
RAF Marham, Norfolk
No 3 Force Protection Wing
15 Squadron, RAF Regiment
RAF Brize Norton, Oxfordshire
No 4 Force Protection Wing
II Squadron (Parachute)
7 RAF Police Squadron
RAF Lossiemouth, Moray
No 5 Force Protection Wing
51 Squadron, RAF Regiment
RAF Coningsby, Lincolnshire
No 7 Force Protection Wing
1 Squadron, RAF Regiment
Air Land Integration Cell
RAF Waddington, Lincolnshire
No 8 Force Protection Wing
63 Squadron (Queen's Colour Squadron), RAF Regiment (RAF Northolt, Middlesex)
1 Tactical Police Squadron (RAF Cranwell)
4 RAF Police (Typhoon) Squadron (RAF Lossiemouth)
5 RAF Police (ISTAR) Squadron (RAF Waddington)
6 RAF Police (Lightning) Squadron (RAF Marham)

family, government, and armed forces from RAF Northolt in the west of London. These Command Support Air Transport (CSAT) aircraft are operated by 32 (The Royal) Squadron. Its veteran fleet of BAe 146 jets and an AgustaWestand A109SP helicopter are in the process of being replaced.

To protect forward deployed aircraft and air bases, the RAF Regiment and RAF Police have a sophisticated array of units. Force Protection Wings combine field squadrons from the RAF Regiment and personnel from the RAF Police into a single organisation at deployed locations.

The RAF Regiment is headquartered at RAF Honington in Suffolk, which is also home to its training depot.

The RAF has a significant deployable Support Force, which is sometimes known as the A4 Force, and this is responsible for the establishment and sustainment of deployed operating bases overseas for exercises and operations.

RAF Wittering, which sits on the Cambridgeshire/Northamptonshire border, is the main operating base and headquarters for the RAF A4 Force. It is able to pull together the vital engineering and logistical support needed to sustain RAF operations and exercises around the world, from explosive ordnance disposal to catering and aircraft repair to ground transport vehicles.

Commanding Air Power – No 11 Group

The historic No 11 Group was reformed in November 2018 to take responsibility for the RAF core command and control organisations, including its deployable Joint Force Air Component (JFAC) headquarters, the National Air & Space Operations Centre (NASOC) and the Battle Management Force. The JFAC and NASOC are both based at RAF High Wycombe.

No 11 Group is responsible for the RAF home-based and deployable Battle Management Force organisation, which is headquartered at RAF Boulmer in Northumberland. It provides radar surveillance of UK

ABOVE: Protecting RAF airfields at home and abroad from a range of threats, including chemical, nuclear, and biological contamination, is the job of the RAF Regiment. (MOD/CROWN COPYRIGHT)

LEFT: Four BAe 146 aircraft filled the Command Support Air Transport (CSAT) role until March 31, 2022. (IGOR BUBIN)

airspace and tactical control of RAF aircraft. It coordinates the operations of Remote Radar Heads (RRH) at

- RRH Benbecula
- RRH Neatishead
- RRH Buchan
- RRH Staxton Wold
- RRH Portreath
- RRH Brizlee Wood

The group has a deployable radar and command/control capability under 1 Air Control Centre. It is currently based at RAF Scampton but will move to RAF Boulmer when its current base closes.

RAF Spadeadam in Cumbria, where the UK's Electronic Warfare Tactics Range is based, is also part of No 11 Group.

The RAF's ballistic missile warning radar site at RAF Fylingdales in North Yorkshire is not part of No 11 Group. It reports to the newly established tri-service UK Space Command. The iconic pyramid Solid State Phased Array RADAR (SSPAR) at RAF Fylingdales is capable of detecting objects the size of a Coke can 3,000 miles into space. It was originally set up in the Cold War to provide early warning of a Soviet nuclear missile attack on Britain. Today it also monitors threats to the UK's growing network of satellites.

Training Pipeline – No 22 Group

No 22 Group is responsible for training all RAF personnel from when they join the service through »

LEFT: VIP transport is provided by 32 (The Royal) Squadron's A109 helicopters. (JAMES GLOUCESTER)

to completing their initial aircrew or ground trade training. The group is also tasked with providing aircrew training for the Royal Navy and Army Air Corps under the umbrella of the Military Flying Training Service (MFTS), which is operated in partnership with the Ascent consortium led by US defence giant Lockheed Martin.

Initial training of RAF officers takes place at the Royal Air Force College at RAF Cranwell in Lincolnshire, and basic training for airmen and airwomen is currently conducted at RAF Halton in Buckinghamshire. Plans are being developed to eventually transition this to a new site at RAF Cranwell.

No 22 Group currently has 3,800 regular military and 1,900 civilian personnel. Each year, No 22 Group trains around 61,000 individuals at various levels across its 53 sites. It also administers the University Air Squadrons from RAF Cranwell.

Ground trade training takes place at RAF Cosford in Shropshire, RAF Digby in Lincolnshire, and the Ministry of Defence site at St Athan in south Wales, as well as at the tri-service Defence College of Technical Training (DCTT) at RAF Lyneham in Wiltshire. This covers a range of trades, including aeronautical engineering, communications and information systems, electrical and mechanical engineering.

The Group is also responsible for the Air Cadet Organisation, which has approximately 41,000 cadets and 12,000 adult volunteers. The RAF's Air Cadets is one of the country's premier youth organisations and the world's largest youth air training organisation, supported by thousands of dedicated volunteer staff. It is composed of the Air Training Corps (ATC), Combined Cadet Force (CCF) RAF sections, Gliding and Air Experience Flying units.

No 22 Group's Directorate of Flying Training provides a wide range of courses that train officers and non-commissioned aircrew to the high standards needed when flying on modern operations. It also trains air traffic controllers and flight operations personnel to meet frontline requirements.

British flying training is run as a pipeline that is controlled centrally by No 22 Group from its headquarters at RAF High Wycombe. After potential aircrew successfully pass a series of selection tests, they progress to elementary training where they learn the basics of airmanship and how to handle light aircraft. Students then graduate with their wings and progress to an operational conversion unit to learn to fly a frontline fixed- or rotary-wing aircraft type. During their progress along the pipeline, student pilots have to move through at least three separate courses on increasingly more complex and demanding airframes until they graduate. Fast jet pilots, for example, undergo 28 weeks of elementary training, 42 weeks of basic training and then 52 weeks of advanced training.

For nearly 20 years the Ministry of Defence has been developing a project to recapitalise its pilot and aircrew training pipeline, including the provision of state-of-the-art training aircraft and simulators, in co-operation with the private sector, using what have been described as 'innovative financial instruments'.

This project was eventually dubbed the Military Flying Training Service (MFTS). It was originally envisaged as involving £6 billion of investment over a 25-year period. In 2008, the US defence giant Lockheed Martin and the UK-based engineering and outsourcing company Babcock – working together under the banner Ascent – won the 25-year Private Finance Initiative (PFI) contract. This would see them first design a more efficient and effective flying training pipeline and then run a procurement exercise to find new equipment and service providers to carry forward MFTS, largely involving outsourcing procurement models.

Once the new equipment and courses were in place, Ascent was charged with working in partnership with No 22 Group to run the operation to the end of the contract's life in the 2030s. The Ministry of Defence was forced to adopt this model to avoid the upfront costs of recapitalising its training aircraft fleet. However, it did mean the whole project was mired in bureaucratic and legal red tape as the various contractors were keen to pin down exactly what they were doing and, crucially, how they would get paid.

Over the past decade, No 22 Group and Ascent have been recapitalising all the aircraft and helicopters operated by MFTS. The Affinity Team of Israel's Elbit Systems and the US defence services firm KBR were selected in October 2014 to provide the new fixed-wing element, based on 23 Grob G 120TP Prefect T1s »

BELOW: The veteran Hawk T1 has been replaced by the Hawk T2 for advanced pilot training. (TIM FELCE)

for elementary flying, 10 Beechcraft Texan T1s for basic flying and five Embraer Phenom T1s for multi-engine pilot training. Advanced jet training continued to be carried out on the BAE Systems Hawk T2s at RAF Valley in Anglesey. The reduced number of basic trainers meant that RAF Linton-upon-Ouse in North Yorkshire had to close, and the Texan entered service at RAF Valley. Elementary training remained at RAF Barkston Heath and RAF Cranwell, both in Lincolnshire.

In parallel to this, Ascent ran a competition to find a new contractor to run the Defence Helicopter Flying School at RAF Shawbury in Shropshire. In 2016 Airbus Helicopters won this £500 million contract that will see them provide nearly 29 Airbus H135 Juno HT1s and three H145 Jupiter HT1 helicopters and also be responsible for the generation of airframes on a daily basis at RAF Shawbury.

The Prefects were the first MFTS fixed-wing aircraft to receive formal Release To Service (RTS) in July 2017 from the Ministry of Defence aviation safety authority. The new helicopters received their RTS in May 2017. Progress on the Phenom was slower after they received RTS on February

2018, and the first courses at RAF Cranwell did not start until January 2019. The first students started training on the Texan in the summer of 2020, and to expand capacity four more of the aircraft were ordered in December 2021.

Rotor Power – Joint Helicopter Command

RAF battlefield helicopters are controlled outside the service's chain of command by the tri-service Joint Helicopter Command (JHC). This organisation is run from Army Headquarters in Andover in Hampshire and senior officers from the Royal Navy, British Army and RAF take turns to command it.

After decades of the country's military helicopters being treated as a Cinderella capability that had no champions within their parent services, the 1998 defence review »

ABOVE: Helicopter pilots from the RAF, FAA and AAC all train on the H145 Jupiter H1 at the Defence Helicopter Flying School at RAF Shawbury in Shropshire. (MOD/CROWN COPYRIGHT)

BELOW: Basic rotary wing training is carried out on H135 Juno HT1 at the Defence Helicopter Flying School at RAF Shawbury. (PAULAKAJACK)

decided that a single two-star headquarters should be set up to control all the battlefield – attack, reconnaissance, and transport – helicopters of the three British armed services.

This has the job of preparing British battlefield helicopters for operations and engages in setting future procurement requirements. It is also responsible for a portfolio of deployable joint headquarters that control all helicopters in operational theatres.

The RAF's contribution to the JHC is the support or transport helicopters based at RAF Odiham in Hampshire and RAF Benson in Oxfordshire, as well as the fuel tankers of the Tactical Supply Wing based in Stafford.

RAF Odiham is home to the Boeing Chinook HC4/5/6 heavy lift helicopters of 18 (Bomber) Squadron and 27 Squadron. The Special Forces-role Chinooks of 7 Squadron are also home based at the station. The Chinook Force has sustained

ABOVE: The Chinook HC6 is configured to conduct long-range missions in support of Special Forces units. (MOD/CROWN COPYRIGHT)

RIGHT: RAF Puma HC2 helicopters are scheduled to be retired in the middle of this decade. (MOD/CROWN COPYRIGHT)

a contingent of helicopters in Mali since 2018 under the codename of Operation Newcombe.

Eurocopter Puma HC2 medium helicopters are based at RAF Benson, along with Chinooks used for operational conversion training by 28 Squadron. Two Puma units, 33 and 230 Squadron, each took turns to deploy to Afghanistan between 2015 and July 2021 but have since been home based. The JHC's Operational Evaluation Unit, 22 Squadron, is based at RAF Benson, along with the Medium Support Helicopter Aircrew Training Facility (MSHATF), which has six helicopter flight simulators representing Chinook and Puma helicopters.

Flying the Flag – Overseas Bases

The formal closure of RAF Brüggen in Germany in 2002 ended the permanent basing of RAF combat aircraft overseas. Since then, the RAF has been an expeditionary air »

ABOVE: RAF helicopter pilots train on simulators at the Medium Support Helicopter Aircrew Training Facility at RAF Benson in Oxfordshire, run by the Canadian company CAE. (MOD/CROWN COPYRIGHT)

force, deploying overseas for exercises and operations. A network of air bases remains in Britain's overseas territories and they are operated by small RAF contingents controlled by the UK's Permanent Joint Headquarters from its command post at Northwood in west London.

The biggest overseas RAF station is inside the UK Sovereign Base area on the eastern Mediterranean island of Cyprus. RAF Akrotiri has only one permanently based flying unit, 84 Squadron, with its Bell Griffin HAR2 search and rescue helicopters. It is now frequently used as a launch pad for British aircraft operating across the Middle East, North Africa, and the Black Sea region.

At the other end of the Mediterranean, RAF Gibraltar is a strategically positioned base that allows the RAF to launch operations into West Africa. Transport aircraft heading to Mali to resupply the British Army and RAF contingents regularly use Gibraltar.

Once it was declared fully operational in February 1986, RAF Mount Pleasant became the British military headquarters in the South Atlantic and the hub for the UK garrison on the Falkland Islands. The air base, 43 kilometres southwest of Port Stanley, cost £215 million to build.

Since then, the heart of the British garrison has been its RAF

fighter jets, which are based inside hardened aircraft shelters and stand ready on 24/7 quick reaction alert duty. Initially these were US-made McDonnell Douglas Phantom FGR2s until they were replaced by Tornado F3s in 1992. In 2009 the first Typhoon jets arrived at RAF Mount Pleasant, and they remain on duty there today. The site is now officially titled the Mount Pleasant Complex. While the Phantom and Panavia Tornado F3s were specialist air defence jets, the Typhoon is a true multi-role aircraft and can take on air, land, and naval threats with a variety of guided weapons. No air force in South America, including Argentina's, has anything to match the Typhoon and its suite of long-range stand-off missiles, making it inconceivable that any invasion force would get anywhere close to the Falklands.

With air supremacy assured over the South Atlantic and its reinforcement air route secured to the RAF-controlled airfield on Ascension Island, Britain has run down the land- and sea-based elements of its Falklands garrison. It is currently home to just under 900 military personnel who live in the massive Mount Pleasant complex. This boasts more than 800 metres of centrally heated corridors, leading to it be nicknamed the 'Death Star' after the

space station in the *Star Wars* movies. The commander of British Forces South Atlantic Islands is now a tri-service one-star appointment, with officers from the three UK armed services taking turns in the chair.

The British Army now only keeps a reinforced infantry company of around 150 troops on the Falklands. It is supported by a similar number of gunners from the Royal Artillery who operate a battery of MBDA Sky Sabre surface-to-air missiles that defend the islands. During 2021 the veteran BAe Dynamics Rapier missiles were replaced by the Sky Sabres to complete the modernisation of the air defences of the Falklands. Early warning of attack is provided by the RAF through a network of radar stations on the island's highest peaks.

A crucial element in sustaining the British garrison on the Falklands is the air bridge provided by RAF aircraft from RAF Brize Norton. To reach the Falklands aircraft have to stage through UK/US run Wideawake Auxiliary Airfield on Ascension Island. Heavy use of this meant that in 2017 the 10,000-foot runway on the island had to be partially closed for repairs that will not be completed until late in 2022. As a temporary measure, the RAF airbridge is being re-routed through the Atlantic island of Cape Verde.

LEFT: Typhoons based at RAF Akrotiri in Cyprus fly missions across the Middle East, eastern Mediterranean and Black Sea regions. (MOD/CROWN COPYRIGHT)

BELOW: The Mount Pleasant Complex in the Falklands is the hub of British military operations in the South Atlantic. (MOD/CROWN COPYRIGHT)

Fleet Air Arm in 2022

Service Overview

Britain's Royal Navy has more than a century's experience of flying aircraft from ships, and it has a reputation for innovation. It was one of the first military services to operate airships in 1909 and, less than a decade later, the Royal Navy commissioned the first ship that could both launch and recover aircraft, HMS *Argus*.

The birth of the aircraft carrier era saw the Royal Naval Air Service transition into the Fleet Air Arm of the Royal Air Force. In May 1939, the Fleet Air Arm returned to the control of the Admiralty, just in time for the start of World War Two. In this conflict Royal Navy aviators scored notable successes, sinking the bulk of the Italian fleet at Taranto, and then inflicting critical damage to the famous German battleship, the *Bismarck*.

The Fleet Air Arm reached its peak in the 1950s and 1960s with the building of angled deck carriers that embarked jet combat aircraft. The Royal Navy also led the way in embarking helicopters armed with torpedoes and depth charges

on warships for anti-submarine missions. Troop-carrying Royal Navy helicopters also conducted the first ship-to-shore air assault during the 1956 Suez crisis.

Defence cuts in the 1960s and 1970s clipped the wings of the Fleet Air Arm but the combination of the Hawker Siddeley Sea Harrier and the Invincible-class carriers proved instrumental to the successful South Atlantic campaign in 1982 that enabled Britain to recapture the Falkland Islands.

From the 1980s through to 2010 the Royal Navy fielded three Invincible-class carriers, but a brutal round of defence cuts led to the scrapping of these iconic ships and the Hawker Siddeley Harrier GR9s that flew from them. This began a decade in which the Fleet Air Arm only operated helicopters from its warships.

In the past decade, the Fleet Air Arm has seen its organisation and structure trimmed back to meet the tight financial circumstances of the era. The old Fleet Air Arm headquarters at Yeovilton Naval Air Station is a memory.

Control of British naval aviation is now split between the Assistant Chief of the Naval Staff (Aviation and Carriers) ACNS (A&C), who controls maritime aviation on warships from Navy Command headquarters in Portsmouth, and the Joint Helicopter Command, which controls the battlefield troop transport helicopters supporting the Royal Marine Commando Forces from Army Headquarters in Andover.

The modern Fleet Air Arm is predominately a rotary-wing force, built around variants of the AgustaWestland Merlin and Wildcat platforms.

To dominate sea zones and hunt submarines, the Merlin HM2 operates from carriers, frigates, destroyers, and shore bases. It has a surveillance radar to look for hostile warships and monitors the undersea environment with sonobuoys and dunking sonar. Extensive communications and datalinks allow it to share combat information with warships, aircraft, and shore bases.

Until 2018, 849 NAS operated the old Westland Sea King ASAC7 in the airborne surveillance and control role, but the Fleet Air Arm is in the process of receiving the new Crowsnest airborne early warning (AEW) system to regenerate this vital capability. This system is intended >>

The Fleet Air Arm is in the process of getting back into the fast jet business almost a decade after the retiring of the Harrier GR9s, with the Lockheed Martin F-35B Lightning II combat jet now operational from the Royal Navy's two new aircraft carriers, HMS *Queen Elizabeth,* and HMS *Prince of Wales.*

UK naval aviation squadrons are held at varying states of readiness to be mobilised for operations.

The largest Royal Navy aviation deployment of 2021 was a cruise by HMS *Queen Elizabeth* and her carrier strike group to the Far East. This saw a sustained deployment of fast jets on the Royal Navy carrier for the first time in over a decade.

Both HMS *Queen Elizabeth* and HMS *Prince of Wales* are now fully operational, and keeping their flight decks full of aircraft and helicopters is a priority of the Fleet Air Arm. There are currently only enough F-35B aircraft, pilots, and maintainers to field one air group at a time, so during 2022 and 2023 it is expected that each carrier will take turns to be at high readiness to embark an F-35B air group. The other carrier will concentrate on being a helicopter platform for Fleet Air Arm, Royal Air Force and Army Air Corps assets.

The Navy X experimental organisation is now in the midst of several projects to bring unmanned aerial vehicles (UAVs) into service. These range from small-scale hand-launched drones that can be operated from Royal Marine landing craft up to large and long endurance systems that can be launched off the deck of the Queen Elizabeth-class carriers by catapult. A possible unmanned replacement for the Crowsnest AEW helicopter is being actively explored.

More than a century after its early experiments operating manned aircraft from the first carriers, the Royal Navy remains at the forefront of developing naval aviation technology.

to be installed as a roll-on, roll-off kit on standard Merlin MH2 airframes but has not yet been formally declared fully operational.

The Royal Navy Wildcat Force has the mission of dominating sea zones around naval task groups. Its helicopters have powerful radars and thermal imaging sensors to monitor surface targets, including small patrol boats. In 2021 it began fielding the new Thales Martlet missile that can be fired in volleys against swarms of enemy patrol boats. The larger MBDA Sea Venom weapon will allow Wildcats to engage bigger warships when it enters service later this decade.

To move Royal Marine assault forces around the battlefield, the Commando Helicopter Force (CHF) is equipped with the Merlin HC3/4. These helicopters are also used for utility tasks within the carrier battlegroup. Some 25 ex-RAF Merlin HC3/3As are now being converted to the HC4/4A configuration under the Merlin Life Sustainment Programme,

which incorporates an HM2 standard cockpit as well as folding blades and tail rotors to allow them to be operated from amphibious warfare ships. The first converted HC4/4A was handed over to the CHF in May 2018 and all the helicopters are expected to be converted by 2023.

Fleet Air Arm Order of Battle

The Fleet Air Arm operates the Royal Navy's helicopters and unmanned aerial vehicles

Royal Navy Fleet Air Arm Squadrons, April 2022				
Unit	**Aircraft**	**Base**	**Role**	**Notes**
Navy Command, Portsmouth				
Flying Squadrons				
809 Naval Air Squadron	F-35B Lightning	RAF Marham	Carrier-borne fighter/strike	To reform in April 2023
814 Naval Air Squadron	Merlin HM2	RNAS Culdrose	Anti-submarine warfare/small ship flight	
815 Naval Air Squadron	Wildcat HMA2	RNAS Yeovilton	Small ship flights	
820 Naval Air Squadron	Merlin HM2	RNAS Culdrose	Anti-submarine warfare/carrier air group	
824 Naval Air Squadron	Merlin HM2	RNAS Culdrose	Conversion Training	
825 Naval Air Squadron	Wildcat HMA2	RNAS Yeovilton	Conversion Training	
700X Naval Air Squadron	various	RNAS Culdrose	Remotely Piloted Aircraft System trials unit	
750 Naval Air Squadron	Avenger T1	RNAS Culdrose	Observer grading and training	
FOST Flight	Dauphin	Cornwall Airport, Newquay	Support to Flag Officer Sea Training	
Non-Flying Squadrons				
1700 Naval Air Squadron		RNAS Culdrose	Flight Deck activities, Logistical and Catering Support, Operations, Engineering Support	
1710 Naval Air Squadron		HMNB Portsmouth	Specialist aircraft repair, modification, and scientific support	
Joint Helicopter Command, Andover				
Commando Helicopter Force, RNAS Yeovilton				
845 Naval Air Squadron	Merlin HC4A/HC4	RNAS Yeovilton	Medium lift	
846 Naval Air Squadron	Merlin HC4A/HC4	RNAS Yeovilton	Medium lift/Merlin HC4 Operational Conversion Unit	
847 Naval Air Squadron	Wildcat AH1	RNAS Yeovilton	Battlefield reconnaissance and support	
Headquarters No 22 Group RAF - Military Flying Training Systems				
703 Naval Air Squadron	Prefect T1	RAF Barkston Heath	Elementary Flying Training	Part of the Defence Elementary Flying Training School
705 Naval Air Squadron	Juno HT1	RAF Shawbury	Basic and Advanced Single Engine helicopter training	Part of Defence Helicopter Flying School
727 Naval Air Squadron	Tutor T1	RNAS Yeovilton	Pilot grading and Air Experience/Elementary Flying Training	Part of the Defence Elementary Flying Training School
RAF Air Warfare Centre, RAF Waddington				
744 Naval Air Squadron	Merlin HM2 Crowsnest & Wildcat HMA2	MoD Boscombe Down	Operational Test and Evaluation	Tri-service unit, formerly Mission Systems and Armament Test and Evaluation Squadron RAF

BELOW LEFT: Wildcat HMA2 helicopters operate from all the Royal Navy's frigates and destroyers.
(MOD/CROWN COPYRIGHT)

BELOW RIGHT: The Merlin HM2 is the mainstay of the Royal Navy anti-submarine capability.
(MOD/CROWN COPYRIGHT)

LEFT: Royal Marine Commandos are flown into battle on board Merlin HC4 support helicopters. (MOD/CROWN COPYRIGHT)

BELOW: Royal Navy helicopter observers are trained on board Avenger T1 to enable them to operate the complex mission systems on Merlin HM2 helicopters. (MOD/CROWN COPYRIGHT)

Fleet Air Arm Inventory, April 2022

	Total
Rotary-wing Platforms	
Dauphin	2
Merlin HM2	30
Merlin HC3/3A/4/4A	25
Wildcat HMA2	28
Fixed-wing Platforms	
Avenger T1	4

Source: UK Armed Forces Equipment and Formations annual report by UK Ministry of Defence

Merlin HM2

In service:	2014 onwards
Used by:	Royal Navy
Manufacturer:	Lockheed Martin (prime contractor), AgustaWestland/Leonardo (platform)
Produced:	2005 to 2014
Number built:	30 converted from Merlin HM1
Crew:	Three to four
Powerplant:	Three Rolls-Royce Turbomeca RTM322-01 turboshaft engines
Max take-off weight:	14,600kg (32,187lb)
Cruise speed:	278km/h (173mph, 150kn)
Range:	833km (518 miles, 450nm)
Endurance:	5 hours
Capacity:	26 troops (38 passengers) or five tonnes of payload or four stretchers (with sonar array removed)

Avionics

Selex Galileo Blue Kestrel 5000 maritime surveillance radar

Active/passive sonobuoys

Thales 2189 dipping sonar array

Armament

Bombs:	Four Sting Ray homing torpedoes or Mk 11 depth charges
Door Guns:	One .50cal machine gun

Wildcat HMA2

In service:	2015 onwards
Used by:	Royal Navy
Manufacturer:	AgustaWestland/Leonardo
Produced:	2009 to 2015
Number built:	28
Crew:	Two pilots
Capacity:	Six passengers, including door gunner
Length:	15.24m (50ft)
Height:	3.73m (12ft 3in)
Max take-off weight:	6,000kg (13,228lb)
Powerplant:	Two LHTEC CTS800-4N turboshaft
Maximum speed:	311km/h (193mph, 168kn)
Range:	777km (483 miles, 420nm)
Endurance:	2hr 15min (4hr 30min with auxiliary fuel tanks)

Armament

Pintle-mounted machine gun, e.g., FN MAG (Army) or Browning M3M (Navy).

Air-to-surface missile systems:

Up to 20x Thales Martlet (Lightweight Multirole Missile), formerly Future Anti-Surface Guided Weapon (Light)

Up to 4×MBDA Sea Venom, formerly Future Anti-Surface Guided Weapon (Heavy),

Sting Ray torpedo and Mk 11 depth charges

Fleet Air Arm Stations and Squadrons in 2022

ABOVE: The Merlin HMA2 is the Royal Navy's main ASW helicopter.
(MOD/CROWN COPYRIGHT)

The modern Fleet Air Arm is grouped at its two remaining main operating bases, Royal Naval Air Station Culdrose, near Helston on the Lizard peninsula in the south of Cornwall, and Royal Naval Air Station, Yeovilton in Somerset.

Culdrose, which is officially titled HMS *Sea Hawk*, is home to some 3,000 naval personnel. Its main fighting forces are the three operational Naval Air Squadrons (NAS) equipped with the Royal Navy's 30 AgustaWestland Merlin HM2 anti-submarine helicopters.

As well as the Merlin squadrons, Culdrose is home to a simulator centre to train Merlin aircrew and a pulse line facility where contractors from Leonardo overhaul the helicopters. The two core Merlin HM2 units, 814 and 820 NAS, spend their time detached to Royal Navy warships, providing anti-submarine protection and surface surveillance. 824 NAS conducts operational aircrew conversion training.

There are also a selection of training and support units at Culdrose. Until recently this included 736 NAS, which flew the Hawker Siddeley Hawk T1/T1A to simulate fixed-wing and missile threats to Royal Navy

warships under training. Culdrose is also home to the Royal Navy's only unit equipped with unmanned aerial vehicles (UAV). 700X NAS operates from the nearby Predannack diversion airfield and it stood up in 2014 to administer teams of operators for the leased Boeing Scan Eagle UAV. Since this system was withdrawn from use by the Royal Navy on cost grounds, the squadron has taken the lead in experimenting with UAVs.

Training of Royal Navy personnel who manage aircraft movements on warships' flight decks and stand ready to respond to accidents are carried out at Culdrose's School of Flight Deck Operations.

HMS *Heron* at Yeovilton is now the Fleet Air Arms largest operational airfield, with some 100 helicopters and 4,300 military personnel and

RIGHT: Naval aviators train to fly under the tri-service Military Flying Training System before returning to the Royal Navy to convert to either the Wildcat or Merlin helicopters.
(MOD/CROWN COPYRIGHT)

civilian support staff based there. The command arrangements at the base are complex as some units are under the direct control of the Royal Navy and others are controlled by the tri-service Joint Helicopter Force. There is also a strong contractor presence running simulators and a depth maintenance facility for the AgustaWestland Wildcat HMA2.

The Royal Navy Wildcat Force is based on two flying squadrons. 815 NAS provides flights of one or two of the 28 Wildcat HMA2 maritime variants embarked on Royal Navy frigates and destroyers. Wildcat crews are trained to fly the helicopters by instructors from 825 NAS.

Dedicated support to the Royal Marines of 3 Commando Brigade is provided by a specialist unit, the Commando Helicopter Force (CHF) based at Yeovilton. It is provided with its own mobile command centre, logistical support, and cargo handling facilities to allow it to operate from Royal Navy amphibious warships or ashore in combat zones. The CHF reports to the tri-service Joint Helicopter Command that controls all the UK's battlefield helicopters.

The CHF's Merlin troop-carrying helicopters are operated by 845 and 846 NAS and can trace their heritage in the commando role back to the 1960s. They are still affectionately known as 'Junglies' from their days operating in the Malaysian jungles. The CHF was for a long time associated with the Westland Sea King HC4, but 845 and 846 NAS are now flying the troop-carrying

LEFT: RNAS Culdrose is the home of the Merlin HMA2 fleet. (MOD/CROWN COPYRIGHT)

variant of AgustaWestland Merlin, which were transferred from the RAF from 2014. The 25 ex-RAF Merlin HC3/3As are now being converted to the HC4/4A configuration under the Merlin Life Sustainment Programme.

The third unit of the CHF is 847 NAS, which operates the land variants of the Wildcat, the AH1. It is closely affiliated with 1 Regiment Army Air Corps, which is also based at Yeovilton and operates the Wildcat AH1, sharing training and maintenance facilities. The Navy and Army Wildcat units share a common pool of 34 air frames.

Yeovilton is home to several other important naval aviation linked units, including 727 NAS which assesses the

suitability of potential naval aviators and provides flight experience for youth organisations. Non-flying training units at the station include the Navy's School of Fighter Control, the School of Aircraft Control, and the Helicopter Underwater Escape Trainer. The station also controls the satellite airfield at nearby Merryfield, which is used for tactical deployment training. The Royal Navy Historic Flight is perhaps the most famous unit at Yeovilton, along with Fleet Air Arm Museum.

Enhancements to the communications and other infrastructure at the UK Royal Navy's (RN) forward operating location at Prestwick International

BELOW: The Hawk T1 of 736 Naval Air Squadron operated from RNAS Culdrose in Cornwall in the target simulation role until it was retired on March 31, 2022. (MOD/CROWN COPYRIGHT)

ABOVE: The Royal Navy's Wildcat HMA2s are based at Yeovilton alongside the British Army and Royal Navy AH1 land variants. (MOD/CROWN COPYRIGHT)

RIGHT: RNAS Yeovilton was the home of the legendary Sea Harrier squadrons until they were retired in 2006. (MOD/CROWN COPYRIGHT)

Airport in southwest Scotland started in March 2020. The facility, formerly known as HMS *Gannet,* was home to RN search and rescue helicopters up to January 2016. It has since been used as a forward maintenance and operating location for RN AgustaWestland Merlin HM2 helicopters supporting the Joint Warrior and Perisher series of naval exercises around the west coast of Scotland, as well as participating in 'Defence of the Clyde' operations to protect the passage of Vanguard-class nuclear-powered ballistic missile submarines to and from their home base in Faslane.

The RN site at Prestwick comprises two hangers, aircraft parking ramps and an administrative building. The enhancements to the RN's site at Prestwick represent continued recognition of the strategic importance of the Clyde estuary to the service.

The Lightning Force (LF) operates the Lockheed Martin F-35B Lightning II combat jet from RAF Marham in Norfolk, where the flying squadrons, training and maintenance elements are all based. This is a fully integrated unit with mixed RAF and RN air and ground crew. Personnel from both services are mixed into the flying squadrons and support elements.

The first flying units of LF, 617 Squadron and 207 Squadron have relocated to RAF Marham to be the first F-35B flying squadron and the F-35B operational conversion unit respectively. These are RAF-badged units but the first Royal Navy-badged

unit, 809 NAS, is to stand up in April 2023. One LF unit, 17 Squadron RAF, is still based in the United States conducting test and evaluation tasks.

The training pipeline for future naval aviators is outside of direct Fleet Air Arm control and is run on behalf of the Ministry of Defence by the RAF Headquarters No 22 Group. A number of units within what is dubbed the UK Military Flying Training Service are badged as Royal Navy squadrons. These include 703 NAS which conducts elementary training at RAF Barkston Heath in Lincolnshire with the Grob Prefect T1. Navy helicopter aircrew train with 705 NAS on the Airbus Juno HT1 at RAF Shawbury in Shropshire and would-be Navy fast jet pilots train on the Beechcraft Texan T1 and BAE Systems Hawk T2 at RAF Valley in Wales. Mission specialist aircrew, dubbed observers in the naval tradition, are trained by 750 NAS at Culdrose on the Beechcraft Avenger T1.

ABOVE: The Commando Helicopter Force and its Merlin HC4 assault helicopters are based at RNAS Yeovilton in Somerset. (MOD/CROWN COPYRIGHT)

LEFT: The differences between the legacy Lynx HAS8 (top) and the Wildcat HMA2 can be seen here. (ALAN WILSON)

HMS *Queen Elizabeth* (RO8)

The Royal Navy's Flagship

The first of the new Queen Elizabeth-class aircraft carriers is named after the World War One-era super-dreadnought battleship, HMS *Queen Elizabeth*. This in turn was named after the Tudor monarch, Queen Elizabeth, who famously oversaw the defeat of the Spanish Armada in 1588. The modern HMS *Queen Elizabeth* carries the battle honours and crest — a Tudor rose — of the original battleship.

She is the largest ever Royal Navy warship and the most expensive surface ship yet built in the United Kingdom. After a decade of development and design work, the formal go-ahead for two 65,000-ton Queen Elizabeth-class aircraft carriers was announced in July 2007. The two ships were contracted to cost £3.9bn. Work began on the construction of HMS *Queen Elizabeth* in July 2009 with the first steel being cut at BAE Systems' Govan shipyard in Glasgow.

The first phase of the project included the fabrication of ship blocks at six shipyards around the UK, which incorporated key structural elements as well as piping and electrical wiring. Each block was then floated on a large barge to Babcock International's Rosyth dockyard in Fife, where the final assembly of the ship was conducted under the umbrella of the Aircraft Carrier Alliance, led by BAE Systems and Babcock.

The first two blocks were welded together at Rosyth in June 2011 and over the next two years the ship took shape. She was 80% complete by September 2013 and was formally named by HMS *Queen Elizabeth* on July 4, 2014. Thirteen days later she

was floated out of the Rosyth dry dock in the shipyard's basin to allow the final fitting out to begin.

This had largely been completed by mid-2017 and on June 26 she was manoeuvred out of the basin into the Firth of Forth to begin her contractors' sea trials. After a brief visit to the Invergordon anchorage the following month to inspect possible damage to her propeller shafts, she set sail for her new home at HM Naval Base Portsmouth and arrived on August 16. The ship was formally accepted by the Royal Navy on December 7 during a ceremony conducted while she was docked at Portsmouth. The final costs of the two Queen Elizabeth-class carriers has now been confirmed by the Ministry of Defence to be £6.1bn.

During February 2018, HMS *Queen Elizabeth* conducted operational sea training in the Western Approaches before heading out across the Atlantic on August 18 to begin deck-landing trials with Lockheed Martin F-35B Lightning II aircraft off the east coast of the United States. The first landing and take-off by a US-owned but British-

ABOVE: F-35B Lightning II Jump Jets are a core part of the HMS *Queen Elizabeth* air group.
(MOD/CROWN COPYRIGHT)

Queen Elizabeth-class	
Displacement	65,000 tons
Length	280m (920ft)
Beam	73m (240ft)
Draught	11m (36ft)
Speed	46km/h (25 kts)
Capacity	1,600, of which 679 are usually the ship's crew
Armament	Three Phalanx CIWS, four 30mm DS30M Mk2 guns and six mini-guns
Aircraft carried	40 aircraft and helicopters (65+ aircraft surge capacity)

piloted F-35B took place on September 25 at the start of the trials process.

After a technology-insertion period in early 2019, which saw the installation of Phalanx close-in weapon and advanced communications systems, the ship sailed for the United States again in August to conduct the first embarkation of the UK-owned F-35Bs of the Royal Air Force's 617 Squadron. Exercise Westlant 2019 also saw the first carrier battlegroup deployment by the Royal Navy in a decade, since the retirement of the Invincible-class carriers.

During the first half of 2020, HMS *Queen Elizabeth* conducted two training cruises in UK home waters to allow more F-35B pilots of 617 Squadron and the operational conversion unit, 207 Squadron, to practise deck operations.

In the autumn of 2020 the ship embarked a squadron of US Marine Corps F-35Bs as well as aircraft from 617 Squadron before joining the Exercise Joint Warrior naval wargames off Scotland. This exercise was a dress rehearsal for the ship's deployment to the Mediterranean, Indian Ocean, and Pacific region in the summer of 2021.

Ahead of this deployment, the Royal Navy formally declared the ship's initial operating capability on January 4, 2021. A few days later the Ministry of Defence announced that as well as embarking the USMC F-35B squadron, the HMS *Queen Elizabeth* would be accompanied by a US Navy Arleigh-Burke-class destroyer, the USS *The Sullivans*, during the Carrier Strike Group 21 deployment to the Far East.

LEFT: HMS *Queen Elizabeth*'s distinctive stern as she leaves Portsmouth for the Carrier Strike Group 21 deployment.
(MOD/CROWN COPYRIGHT)

HMS *Prince of Wales* (RO9)

The Royal Navy's Second Aircraft Carrier

RIGHT: HMS *Prince of Wales* sports the famous crest of the heir apparent to the British throne.
(TIM RIPLEY)

The sister ship of HMS *Queen Elizabeth* is named after the World War Two battleship HMS *Prince of Wales*, which was famously sunk in December 1941 off the coast of Malaya by Japanese torpedo bombers. She is the eighth Royal Navy warship to bear the name, which is the title traditionally given to the heir apparent to the British throne.

Since the sinking of the previous HMS *Prince of Wales*, no vessels have carried the name, such was the shock at the loss of the battleship in the dark days before the fall of Britain's imperial bastion of Singapore.

The Queen Elizabeth-class carriers were built deliberately as a pair so that one would always be ready for operations. HMS *Prince of Wales* was constructed to the same basic design as HMS *Queen Elizabeth* and

was assembled in the same shipyard in Fife using the same modular construction process.

Work on HMS *Prince of Wales* began in May 2011 with the first steel being cut at BAE Systems' Govan shipyard in Glasgow. The first blocks arrived at Babcock's Rosyth yard in September 2014 and assembly accelerated until she was floated out of the dry dock into the basin to allow the final fitting out towards the end of 2017.

She was ready to sail on September 29, 2019 and passed out of the basin into the Firth of Forth to begin her contractors' sea trials. Once the carrier had arrived at HM Naval Base Portsmouth she was formally commissioned into the Royal Navy. In February 2020, the ship made a week-long visit to the port of Liverpool and hosted thousands of visitors on

BELOW: HMS *Prince of Wales* awaits the arrival of her helicopter-focussed air group before heading to Exercise Cold Response off Norway in March 2022.
(MOD/CROWN COPYRIGHT)

board in a major exercise in public engagement.

A few weeks later, HMS *Prince of Wales* suffered the first of two floodings in her engine room. The second flood caused major damage to electrical cabling and the electrical generator that transferred power to her propellers. Although at the time the Royal Navy described the flooding as 'minor', by the end of 2020 the damage was revealed to be serious and this resulted in the indefinite cancellation of the carrier's deployment to the east coast of the US for Lockheed Martin F-35B Lightning II Jump Jet trials. The repairs to the engines were said to be expected to last at least six months. It was also revealed that the ship only spent a total of 30 days at sea in 2020.

Ever since work began on HMS *Prince of Wales* it had been under threat of cancellation on cost grounds. The ship survived the 2010 UK Defence Review but only on with the proviso that a full decision on bringing her into service would be put off to a later date. Once completed the carrier was to be placed in temporary storage.

ABOVE: The sail of HMS *Prince of Wales* against the backdrop of the *Aurora Borealis* during a visit to the Arctic Circle for Exercise Cold Response in March 2022.
(MOD/CROWN COPYRIGHT)

The defence review had committed the Royal Navy to fitting electro-magnetic catapults and arrester hooks to allow the Queen Elizabeth-class carriers to operate the arrester hook-fitted version of the Lightning, the F-35C. However, as work on HMS *Queen Elizabeth* was too far advanced, it was decided that HMS *Prince of Wales* would be the first to be fitted with the electro-magnetic catapult and the first carrier could be retrofitted during her first major refit at some point in the future. These plans were thrown into turmoil in 2012 when cost overruns and technical delays to the US-made Electro Magnetic Launch Systems, known as EMALS, forced the Ministry of Defence to cancel the project and complete the HMS *Prince of Wales* with a ski jump so she could operate the F-35B.

The UK's 2015 Defence Review reversed the position of the previous review and the Royal Navy was committed to operating HMS *Prince of Wales* alongside her sister ship, either as a strike carrier or in the amphibious assault role with transport helicopters and Royal Marines embarked. In April, 2022 she returned to Portsmouth having functioned as NATO command ship throughout Cold Response, the largest winter exercise hosted in Norway in more than 30 years.

LEFT: A full-frontal view of HMS *Prince of Wales* and her ski jump.
(MOD/CROWN COPYRIGHT)

Queen Elizabeth-class	
Displacement	65,000 tons
Length	280m (920ft)
Beam	73m (240ft)
Draught	11m (36ft)
Speed	46km/h (25 kts)
Capacity	1,600, of which 679 are usually the ship's crew
Armament	Three Phalanx CIWS, four 30mm DS30M Mk2 guns and six mini-guns
Aircraft carried	40 aircraft and helicopters (65+ aircraft surge capacity)

Army Aviation in 2022

Service Overview

ABOVE: Eight Apache attack helicopters of 3 Regiment Army Air Corps during Exercise Talon Gravis in Suffolk in 2019.
(MOD/CROWN COPYRIGHT)

BELOW: The Royal Artillery operates the British Army's Watchkeeper tactical unmanned aerial vehicles.
(MOD/CROWN COPYRIGHT)

The British Army can claim to have pioneered the use of aircraft for military purposes in Britain with the establishment of the Royal Flying Corps in 1912. This had grown out of the hot air balloon battalion of the Royal Engineers and within two years the first British aircraft were duelling with German opponents over France.

With the establishment of the Royal Air Force in 1918, the British Army lost its own air component for nearly 40 years. During World War Two the first Army Air Corps (AAC)

was formed but it did not have its own powered aircraft. Its core was the airborne troops of the Parachute Regiment and the personnel of the Glider Pilot Regiment who, as the name suggests, flew into battle in gliders. Royal Artillery spotters were also assigned to work within RAF Air Observation Post (AOP) Squadrons.

This convoluted arrangement came to an end in 1957 when the modern day AAC was formed to incorporate the old RAF AOP squadrons with new units that would fly helicopters. These revolutionary machines were entering

widespread use across the world and were set to transform warfare in the Vietnam conflict.

The British AAC received a major boost in the 1970s when the TOW anti-tank missile-armed Westland Lynx AH1 entered service. The Royal Artillery remained in the aviation business in the 1970s and 1980s through its use of Canadair CL-289 unmanned aerial vehicles to spot targets for its guns and rockets. This separation of manned and unmanned aviation continued until 2016 when 47 Regiment Royal Artillery, which operates the Thales Watchkeeper WK450 tactical unmanned aerial vehicle, was transferred to the control of the Joint Helicopter Command (JHC). This tri-service organisation controls all AAC, Royal Navy and RAF battlefield helicopters. However, the AeroVironment RQ-20 Puma and Wasp III UAV mini-UAVs operated by 32 Regiment Royal Artillery remain outside the JHC and are controlled by British Army ground units.

The British Army's aviation branch has been transformed over the past 20 years since the introduction of the AgustaWestland Apache AH1 attack helicopter. Their successful deployment to Afghanistan from 2006 cemented the place of the AAC as one of the British Army's combat arms.

Over the past decade the AgustaWestland Wildcat AH1 has entered service to replace the veteran Westland Lynx as the AAC's primary utility and observation helicopter.

In 2020 the British Army set up a new formation, 1 Aviation Brigade, to control all the Apache and Wildcat squadrons, as well as dedicated logistics and maintenance units to enable the brigade to be deployed into the field as a self-contained entity. The brigade is destined to cooperate with the soon to be set up Deep Recce Strike Brigade Combat Team, working alongside Royal Artillery Multiple Launch Rocket System (MLRS) batteries and formation reconnaissance regiments equipped with the Ajax family of vehicles. This is a signal of the British Army's intention to harness the power of its aviation assets to achieve decisive

effect on conventional combat operations against peer opponents.

The AAC operates several helicopters in non-combat roles in the UK and around the world, including Gazelles in Northern Ireland and Bell 212s in Brunei. A squadron of Eurocopter Dauphin helicopters painted in civilian markings are used to support the Special Air Service on counter-terrorist missions around the United Kingdom. The 2021 defence review called time on these small AAC units and set in train a project to purchase replacement modern helicopters that will also be used by the Royal Air Force in a variety of roles.

The AAC is in the process of replacing its old Apache AH1 with the new Boeing Apache AH2 variant, which is known as the AH-64E, or 64 Echo in the US, which features improved weapons, sensors and engines to make it more lethal and survivable on the battlefields of the future. Contracts were placed for the first 50 of the improved helicopters in July 2016. Unlike the original British variant of the Apache, which were assembled by Westland Helicopters in Yeovil, the majority of the work on the new variant is being carried out at Boeing's plant at Mesa in Arizona. The aim is to keep the British helicopters as similar to their US »

ABOVE: The thermal imaging and radar sensors of the Apache AH1 give it the ability to find and engage targets day and night. (MOD/CROWN COPYRIGHT)

BELOW: Army Air Corps units regularly train to operate from deployed locations. (MOD/CROWN COPYRIGHT)

Army counterparts as possible to reduce manufacturing costs and allow future upgrades to be made efficiently.

The core fuselage, Longbow radar and many other smaller components from old Apache AH1s are being recycled for use in the new helicopters. Known as the AH-64E Version 6, the new helicopter features more powerful General Electric T700-GE-701D engines, new transmissions, new composite rotor blades and improved landing gear.

The other main helicopter in use by the AAC is the Wildcat AH1, which is proving to be a robust and worthy successor to the veteran army variant of the old Lynx. In what became a rather convoluted procurement process, in 2004 the UK Ministry of Defence eventually settled on a single airframe fulfilling the needs of both the British Army and Royal Navy. This decision led to the development of what was initially called the Future Lynx or Lynx Wildcat. Two main variants went into service, with the land variant dubbed the Wildcat AH1 and the maritime variant designated the Wildcat HMA2.

The two variants share a common airframe, engine, drive train and defensive aid suite but have different sensors and weapons. Both versions have the large L-3 Wescam MX-15Di electro-optical/infrared turret mounted in the nose but the maritime variants have the SELEX Galileo Seaspray 7000E Active Electronically Scanned Array (AESA) radar. The armament of the land variant is less

well armed with its only offensive capability being a 0.50 cal heavy machine gun that can be positioned in a cabin door mounting for self defence.

The British Army's Watchkeeper eye in the sky first flew in 2010 but technical issues delayed its full entry to service until the end of 2018. It was originally ordered in 2005 to replace the obsolete GEC Marconi Phoenix

drone and was based on the design of the Hermes 450 unmanned aerial vehicle (UAV), which is made by the Israeli company Elbit. In partnership with the French company, Thales, Elbit set up a factory in Leicester to assemble the Watchkeeper systems for the British Army.

Urgent demands for aerial surveillance from commanders in

Iraq and Afghanistan meant the British Army ended up leasing several Hermes 450s until the Watchkeepers were ready for action. A handful of prototype Watchkeepers were sent to Afghanistan in 2014 to fly patrols and monitor the final withdrawal of British troops, using the UAV's electro-optical and synthetic aperture radar sensors.

ABOVE: Wildcat reconnaissance and utility helicopters are often teamed with Apache attack helicopters to scout for targets. (MOD/CROWN COPYRIGHT)

LEFT: Air Troopers are AAC non-commissioned officers who crew the rear cabin of Wildcat AH1 helicopters and operate the door guns. (NATO)

Army Aviation Order of Battle

The Army Air Corps and Royal Artillery operates the British Army helicopters and unmanned aerial vehicles

ABOVE: AAC Apache AH1 attack helicopters are true joint assets and routinely train and operate on Royal Navy aircraft carriers or alongside RAF aircraft. (MOD/CROWN COPYRIGHT)

ABOVE: Battlefield surveillance is the primary task of the AAC's Wildcat AH1s. (MOD/CROWN COPYRIGHT)

ABOVE: The AAC's Bell 212s provide training support to British Army units in Brunei and elsewhere. (MOD/CROWN COPYRIGHT)

Army Air Corps Inventory, April 2022	
	Total
Rotary-wing Platforms	
Apache AH1	30
Apache AH2	14
Bell 212	5
Gazelle AH1	26
Wildcat AH1	34
Dauphin	6
Royal Artillery Inventory, April 2022	
Unmanned Aerial Vehicles	
Watchkeeper	46
Source: UK Armed Forces Equipment and Formations annual report by UK Ministry of Defence	

Army Air Corps and Royal Artillery Aviation Units, April 2022				
Unit	**Sub-Units**	**Helicopter**	**Role**	**Location**
Joint Helicopter Command/Army Headquarters				
1 Combat Aviation Brigade Combat Team				
1 Regiment AAC	651 Squadron AAC	??	??	RNAS Yeovilton, Somerset
	652 Squadron AAC	Wildcat AH1	Training/Conversion Unit	RNAS Yeovilton
	659 Squadron AAC	Wildcat AH1	Surveillance and Utility	RNAS Yeovilton
	661 Squadron AAC	Wildcat AH1	Surveillance and Utility	RNAS Yeovilton
3 Regiment AAC	653 Squadron AAC	Apache AH1/2	Attack/Training	Wattisham Flying Station, Suffolk
	662 Squadron AAC	Apache AH1/2	Attack	Wattisham Flying Station
	663 Squadron AAC	Apache AH1/2	Attack	Wattisham Flying Station
4 Regiment AAC	656 Squadron AAC	Apache AH1	Attack	Wattisham Flying Station
	664 Squadron AAC	Apache AH1	Attack	Wattisham Flying Station

Army Air Corps and Royal Artillery Aviation Units, April 2022				
Unit	**Sub-Units**	**Helicopter**	**Role**	**Location**
5 Regiment AAC	665 Squadron AAC	Gazelle AH1	Surveillance and Utility	Aldergrove Flying Station, County Antrim
	667 Squadron AAC	Bell 212	Utility	Brunei
6 Regiment AAC	675 (The Rifles) Squadron		Aviation support	Yeovil/Taunton, Somerset
	677 (Suffolk and Norfolk Yeomanry (Squadron)		Aviation support	Blenheim Camp, Bury St Edmunds, Suffolk
	678 (The Rifles) Squadron		Aviation support	Milton Keynes/Luton, Bedfordshire
	679 (The Duke of Connaught's) Squadron		Aviation support	Middle Wallop, Hampshire
7 Aviation Support Battalion, Royal Electrical and Mechanical Engineers (REME)			Attack Helicopter Support	Wattisham Flying Station
Army Aviation Centre				Middle Wallop
7 (Training) Regiment AAC	670 Squadron		Operational Training	Middle Wallop
	671 Squadron	Wildcat AH1, Gazelle AH1, Bell 212	Conversion to type	Middle Wallop
	673 Squadron	Apache AH1	Conversion to type	Middle Wallop
Intelligence, Surveillance and Reconnaissance Group, Larkhill				Larkhill, Wiltshire
47 Regiment RA	31 (Headquarters) Battery		Command and Control	Horne Barracks, Larkhill
	10 (Assaye) Battery	Watchkeeper WK450 TUAS	Surveillance	Horne Barracks, Larkhill
	43 Battery (Lloyd's Company)	Watchkeeper WK450 TUAS	Surveillance	Horne Barracks, Larkhill
	57 (Bhurtpore) Battery	Watchkeeper WK450 TUAS	Surveillance	Horne Barracks, Larkhill
	74 Battery (The Battle Axe Company)	Watchkeeper WK450 TUAS	Surveillance	Horne Barracks, Larkhill
32 Regiment RA	46 (Talavera) Headquarters Battery		Command and Control	Roberts Barracks, Larkhill
	18 (Quebec 1759) Battery	Puma and Wasp Mini UAV	Surveillance	Roberts Barracks, Larkhill
	21 (Gibraltar 1779–83) Air Assault Battery	Puma and Wasp Mini UAV	Surveillance Support to 16 Air Assault Brigade	Roberts Barracks, Larkhill
	22 (Gibraltar 1779–83) Battery	Puma and Wasp Mini UAV	Surveillance	Roberts Barracks, Larkhill
Headquarters No 22 Group RAF - Military Flying Training Systems				
No. 1 Flying Training School RAF	660 Squadron AAC	Juno HT1	Initial pilot training	RAF Shawbury, Shropshire
Directorate of Special Forces/Joint Special Forces Aviation Wing				
	658 Squadron AAC	Dauphin	Special Forces Support	Stirling Lines, Credenhill, Herefordshire

ABOVE: Aerial surveillance in high threat environments is conducted by the Royal Artillery's Watchkeeper tactical unmanned aerial vehicles. (MOD/CROWN COPYRIGHT)

ABOVE: The veteran Gazelle AH1 is finally being phased out of service after nearly 48 years of service with the AAC. (MOD/CROWN COPYRIGHT)

ABOVE: Special Forces soldiers are flown to incidents in the United Kingdom by Dauphin helicopters of 658 Squadron AAC. (MARK HARKIN)

Watchkeeper WK450 Tactical Unmanned Aerial Vehicle	
In service:	2014 to present
Manufacturer:	UAV Tactical Systems (U-TacS), a joint venture between Elbit Systems and the Thales Group
Produced:	2005 to date
Number built:	54 air vehicles, 46 in service
Specifications	
Powerplant:	UAV Engines Limited R802/902(W) Wankel engine
Length:	6.5m (21ft 3in)
Wingspan:	10.9m (35ft 7in)
Take-off weight:	485kg (1069lb)
Gross weight:	550kg (1,213lb)
Fuel capacity:	105kg (231lb)
Range from ground station:	150km (93 miles)
Cruise speed:	88.6km/h (48kts)
Altitude:	4876.8m (16,000ft)
Aircraft endurance:	14 hours
Ceiling:	5,500m (18,000ft)

Apache AH2 Attack Helicopter	
In service:	2020 onwards
Used by:	British Army
Manufacturer:	Boeing
Produced:	2015 to 2024
Number built:	50 on order for the Army Air Corps, 14 delivered
Specifications	
Powerplant:	T700-GE-701D engines
Length:	14.68m (48.16ft)
Height:	4.72m (15.49ft)
Rotor Diameter:	14.63m (48ft)
Maximum Operating Weight:	10,432kg (23,000lb)
Maximum Level Flight Speed:	279+km/h (150+kts)
Crew:	Two
Armament	
Guns:	M230 Chain Gun, 1,200 rounds
Missiles:	AGM-114 Hellfire, Joint Air-to-Ground Missile (JAGM)
Rockets:	Hydra 70

Army Air Corps and Royal Artillery in 2022

Airpower Profile

RIGHT: Wattisham Flying Station in Suffolk is home to the British Army's Apache attack helicopter regiments. (MOD/CROWN COPYRIGHT)

The AAC's helicopters are concentrated at two main operating bases, with the AgustaWestland Apache AH1 Attack Helicopters (AH) at Wattisham Flying Station in Suffolk and the AgustaWestland Wildcat AH1s at the Royal Naval Air Station Yeovilton in Somerset, alongside the Royal Navy's Wildcat HMA2s.

Each of the AAC's three helicopter regiments are configured to deploy on operations as the core element of an aviation task force and are able to take under command a mix of ground troops, support elements, AAC helicopters and RAF and RN support helicopters. These task forces have to be ready to self-deploy to locations in Europe, via RAF aircraft or RN ships around the world, or to embark onto Queen Elizabeth-class aircraft carriers.

Within the AH Force there is a readiness cycle, with each of the two AH Regiments taking turns to be at 'readiness for operations'. Under this concept, each AAC regimental headquarters is on alert to deploy for a year at a time. The

BELOW: Middle Wallop in Hampshire hosts the Army Aviation Centre and the Army Flying Museum. (JERRY GUNNAR)

operational regiment's two squadrons are also held at readiness or alert to support rapid reaction units, with one squadron at very high readiness (VHR) to deploy to support the Special Forces in either the UK or overseas. Since early 2015, the VHR unit has been called forward to RAF Akrotiri in Cyprus to support UK Special Forces participating in Operation Shader in Iraq and Syria. Not much is known about this detachment's operations but its helicopters are clearly visible on Google Earth satellite imagery of RAF Akrotiri.

Within the Wildcat Force a similar cycle is maintained, with the two operational squadrons taking turns to be at high readiness for operations. A small cadre of experienced pilots and crews at Yeovilton are also held at readiness to support Special Forces operations within the UK or overseas.

In the 2015 annual Ministry of Defence spending round, it was decided to scale back the size of the AH Force. The operational fleet was reduced from 67 to 50 airframes, with the surplus aircraft being cannibalised for spares. At the same time the number of frontline operational squadrons was reduced by two to four squadrons, with 3 Regiment's 653 Squadron being redesignated as the aircrew operational conversion unit. The Apache AH1 is now in the process of being withdrawn from service as the new AH-64E comes online.

In a bid to save money on training and logistics, the Ministry of Defence

ABOVE: Royal Naval Air Station Yeovilton is the home of the AAC Wildcat AH1 fleet. (MOD/CROWN COPYRIGHT)

ordered that both the land and maritime variants of the Wildcat would be based on a single site at Yeovilton Naval Air Station in Somerset. This allows the maintenance of the Wildcat fleet to be carried out by contractors on a single site, and joint training for aircrew also takes place there. The centralised location provides stability for AAC and FAA personnel operating the helicopter.

All the land variants are now operated as a single fleet or pool that is shared by 1 Regiment AAC and 847 Naval Air Squadron. The original intention had been to form five AAC

Wildcat squadrons, but in 2017, in a further round of army reorganisation, this was cut to just three squadrons in a single regiment. This happened halfway through the process to convert 1 and 9 Regiment AAC to operate the Wildcat. The manpower assigned to operate the Wildcat helicopter was therefore reduced. Two sub-units, 669 and 672 Squadron, which had flown the old Westland Lynx AH7 and AH9 until 2017, would not now be reformed to convert to the new helicopter.

The AAC now only has two operational Wildcat sub-units, »

BELOW: Wildcat AH1s are routinely deployed to field locations, such as the north of Norway, to train AAC personnel in operating far from their home bases. (MOD/CROWN COPYRIGHT)

661 and 659 Squadrons, and 652 Squadron is the training/conversion sub-unit for the land variant. There was not expected to be a reduction in the number of Wildcats operated by the AAC and FAA on a day-to-day basis. In December 2019 the Ministry of Defence revealed in a Freedom of Information request that on a daily basis 24 Wildcat AH1 would be operational with the remaining 10 undergoing routine depth maintenance.

Until April 2020, 1 Regiment had been part of an organisation known as the Aviation Reconnaissance Force, or ARF, which controlled the Westland Gazelle AH1s of 5 Regiment AAC and the British Army's fixed wing aircraft at Aldergrove Flying Station in Northern Ireland. The ARF was supposed to be the British Army's 'eyes in the sky' over the UK and on foreign operations. The formation of the 1 Combat Aviation Brigade in April 2020 replaced the ARF, which

meant the Wildcats were placed in this organisation alongside the AAC's Apache AH1 attack helicopters.

1 Regiment AAC is closely integrated with 847 Naval Air Squadron, sharing maintenance, simulator, and conversion training. Personnel are often shared between the two units to help with career planning and build up operational experience. The main difference is that personnel from 847 Squadron have to be qualified to fly their helicopters from the decks of Royal Navy warships to support amphibious landings by the Royal Marines. To fulfil these missions, 847 Squadron is under the day-to-day control of the Commando Helicopter Force (CHF), which is also based at Yeovilton. This ensures close integration with AgustaWestland Merlin HC4s of 845 and 846 Naval Air Squadrons.

5 Regiment AAC in Northern Ireland remains the sole AAC unit operating the veteran Gazelle AH1 observation helicopter. It emerged in January 2022 that five Airbus H135 light helicopters are to be purchased to allow the Gazelles to be retired in 2024.

The Army Aviation Centre at Middle Wallop in Hampshire is the main headquarters of the AAC and hosts several training units, some of which prepare aircrew who have undergone initial training for operational flying at the Defence Helicopter Flying School at RAF Shawbury in Shropshire. This is very different from the role of the JHC

its base at Larkhill. Local flying is conducted from the nearby Ministry of Defence's Boscombe Down airfield and pilot training takes place at RAF Akrotiri in Cyprus, where the Mediterranean climate ensures flying can take place all year round. Test and evaluation flying is conducted from QinetiQ's airfield at Aberporth in west Wales.

In the summer of 2020, 47 Regiment was deployed on its first operational missions to monitor the English Channel for boats carrying migrants towards Dover from France. A forward operating location was set up at Lydd Airport in Kent for the patrols over the Channel.

Small detachments of mini-UAVs from 32 Regiment are routinely assigned to operate with British Army infantry and armoured battlegroups on training grounds around the UK and overseas. This unit reports to 1 Intelligence, Surveillance and Reconnaissance Brigade, alongside other signals intelligence and target acquisition units.

ABOVE: Aberporth Airfield in Ceredigion in Wales was used for trials and development flights of the Watchkeeper system. (MOD/CROWN COPYRIGHT)

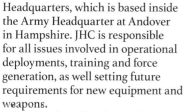

Headquarters, which is based inside the Army Headquarter at Andover in Hampshire. JHC is responsible for all issues involved in operational deployments, training and force generation, as well setting future requirements for new equipment and weapons.

The Royal Artillery's UAV force is concentrated on Salisbury Plan in Wiltshire, within the Larkhill Garrison complex. The Thales Watchkeeper WK450 is now operated by 47 Regiment Royal Artillery from

BELOW: The AAC's fleet of Defender and Islander aircraft were retired from service and sold off after long and faithful service. (MOD/CROWN COPYRIGHT)

Typhoon FRG4

Keeping the RAF Frontline Combat Force Ready for Action

Enhancements to the RAF Eurofighter Typhoon FGR4 fleet are continuing to keep the aircraft combat relevant until the end of the 2030s.

The current focus is on installing an Active Electronically Scanned Array (AESA) radar on the aircraft to transform its ability to detect targets at long range and allow it to operate in complex electronic warfare environments.

British BAE Systems teamed up with the UK arm of the Italian aerospace firm Leonardo to develop the new European Common Radar System Mark 2 (ECRS Mk2) radar for both the RAF's and Italian Air Force's Typhoon aircraft.

The UK element is being funded under a £317m contract and the product is being offered for export.

"It will equip RAF pilots with the ability to locate, identify and suppress enemy air defences using high-powered jamming," said

BAE Systems. "They can engage targets whilst beyond the reach of threats — even when they're looking in another direction — and operate inside the range of opposing air defences, remaining fully protected throughout." The radar will also enable the aircraft to "link up with future data-driven weapons to combat rapidly evolving air defences".

Leonardo is to deliver initial system hardware to BAE Systems' Warton facility in Lancashire in 2022 for aircraft integration and flight trials.

Current planning covers the retrofit of up to 40 Royal Air Force Tranche 3 Typhoons during the second half of the 2020s, with prospects of Tranche 2 retrofits and similar programmes for the Italian Air Force.

ECRS Mk 2 is essentially a new radar. The interface with the aircraft —including attack computer, power and cooling — remains the same, but much of the hardware is of a new design. The multi-function antenna array has more transmit/receive modules with a mix of gallium arsenide (GaAs) and gallium nitride (GaN) elements. It has a rotating drum-type repositioner, as first employed by the Leonardo ES-05 Raven radar developed for the Saab Gripen E/F.

A new processor, new receiver and dedicated electronic warfare receiver and techniques generator are installed, greatly expanding the system's detection capabilities while also adding the ability to conduct electronic attack and jamming in the defence-suppression role. A new radome, being developed by the British company Meggitt, is also required for the aircraft to cater to the radar's wider bandwidth.

Although the RAF Typhoon's weapons capabilities have been dramatically enhanced over the past decade under Project Centurion, work in this area continues. The Block 4 standard MBDA Advanced Short Range Air-to-Air Missile (ASRAAM) is currently in use on Typhoon. It is to be replaced progressively by the upgraded Block 6 missile that incorporates a UK-manufactured seeker. The Block

ABOVE: An impressive performance was put on show by the Typhoon Display Team in 2021. (MOD/CROWN COPYRIGHT)

LEFT: Typhoons launched the Storm Shadow cruise missile in action for the first time in March 2021 against targets in Iraq. (MOD/CROWN COPYRIGHT)

6 seeker underperformed in testing and remedial work delayed the operational evaluation, which in turn delaying entry into service on Typhoon until spring 2022.

The SPEAR Cap 4 mid-life upgrade to the RAF's MBDA Storm Shadow long range, deep penetrating, precision strike weapon is underway. It involves a refreshing of the weapon's explosive components and an upgrade of other components to support service until the end of the decade. The SPEAR 4 variant was accepted into service in January 2022 and will gradually replace the existing stockpile of legacy Storm Shadow weapons.

A drawdown in the strength of the RAF Typhoon fleet was ordered by the 2021 Integrated Review of defence and security. This will see the retiring of the last of the 53 Tranche 1 Typhoons, leaving only 107 Tranche 2 and 3 aircraft in service.

Eurofighter Typhoon FRG4	
In service:	2003 onwards
Used by:	Royal Air Force
Manufacturer:	Eurofighter GmbH/BAE Systems
Produced:	1994 to date
Number built:	160, with 107 still in service
Specifications	
Length:	15.96m (52ft 4in)
Wingspan:	10.95m (35ft 11in)
Max takeoff weight:	23,500kg (51,809lb)
Maximum speed:	2,125km/h (1,320mph, 1,147kts) / Mach 2.0
Combat range:	1,389km (863 miles, 750nm)
Armament	
Guns:	1 × 27 mm Mauser BK-27 revolver cannon with 150 rounds LITENING III laser targeting pod
Air-to-air missiles:	AIM-120 AMRAAM Meteor ASRAAM
Air-to-ground missiles/bombs:	Brimstone guided air-to-ground missile Storm Shadow cruise missile Paveway II/III/Enhanced Paveway series of laser-guided bombs (LGBs) 500-lb Paveway IV

F-35B Lightning

A New Jump Jet for the 21st century

ABOVE: The F-35B Lightning is the only in-production vertical take-off and landing combat aircraft in the world.
(MOD/CROWN COPYRIGHT)

RIGHT: RAF F-35Bs have deployed to Nellis AFB in Nevada for Exercise Red Flag.
(MOD/CROWN COPYRIGHT)

The return of 617 Squadron's Lockheed Martin F-35B Lightning II Jump Jets to RAF Marham in Norfolk in December 2021 after the Carrier Strike Group 21 deployment was the culmination of nearly 20 years of work and an investment of more than £9bn in planes, infrastructure, and people.

Bringing the F-35B into service with the Royal Air Force and Royal Navy has been the most costly and ambitious military aerospace procurement project in recent history. It has seen UK government and the aerospace industry partner with their US counterparts to field Britain's first purpose-designed stealth and vertical take-off and landing aircraft. The F-35B's revolutionary lift fan system has added another layer of complexity to the project. On top of that, the F-35B procurement has been closely intertwined with the Royal Navy's £6bn next-generation aircraft carrier project.

The story of Britain's involvement in what was then known as the Joint Strike Fighter programme has its origins in early work by the Royal Navy to replace its old Invincible-class aircraft carriers. The first future carrier concepts were unveiled in 1997 in a bid to get the newly elected Labour government to approve them in its Strategic Defence Review. As the new carriers were projected as being in service for 40 to 50 years, the Fleet Air Arm

and RAF would need a replacement for the Hawker Siddeley Sea Harrier FA2 and Harrier GR7 Jump Jets then in service. The RAF was also looking to acquire a true stealth or low observable manned aircraft to augment its strike jets.

At the same time, the US military was working on a family of aircraft that could eventually replace a large slice of the US Air Force, US Navy and US Marine Corps manned tactical aircraft fleets. Pentagon chiefs wanted to replace six aircraft types – AV-8B, F-16s, A-10s, FA-18C/Ds, F-15Cs and F-15Es – with one common airframe that could be modified to conduct service-specific missions.

The British government and the newly formed BAE Systems were keen to join the Joint Strike Fighter project. The Ministry of Defence saw the JSF as a strong contender to fly off its new aircraft carriers. So, the British government became a fully fledged partner in the JSF programme, ultimately investing some £2bn to become a Level One partner with a vote on the design specifications of the aircraft. BAE Systems in turn became a Level One partner with the JSF prime contractor, Lockheed Martin, and was guaranteed some 15% of the work on all the 6,000 aircraft that were envisaged as being built over the life of the programme. The Pentagon and BAE Systems invested hundreds of millions of pounds in building three large assembly and machine halls at Samlesbury in Lancashire where the rear fuselage assemblies for every F-35 would be build.

Once Lockheed Martin and its X-35 design had won the JSF contract in 2001 the project moved into the development phase to build flying prototypes and then production F-35 aircraft.

Everything about the F-35 programme is big. More than 3,000 are required by the US military and a similar number are projected for export, making it the biggest military aircraft programme of the 21st century. The UK's chunk of the F-35 programme also generates some massive numbers. The National Audit Office estimated the cost of buying and operating the first batch of 48 aircraft will be £5.8bn by 2024. When the development, support and infrastructure costs are included, the price tag for the UK's F-35s project is estimated by the National Audit Office to be more than £9bn.

The ambition is eventually to have four frontline UK F-35 units, although the plans for the final two operational squadrons are still at an early stage.

Current plans are funded for the purchase of 48 aircraft through to 2024. This breaks down into 12 for each of the frontline squadrons. One squadron will be embarked, or held ready to embark, on the carrier that is at high readiness for operations on a 24/7 basis. Another dozen aircraft will be used for pilot conversion and ground crew training in the UK and the US. The remaining aircraft are expected be undergoing overhaul and a handful will be kept in the US for test and evaluation.

The UK government originally declared its intention to purchase 138 F-35 aircraft, which will provide the planes for two more squadrons in the Lightning Force and then provide the RAF with a shore-based capability. These plans are not set in stone, however, and there is little money for them long term in the Ministry of Defence's budget.

ABOVE: HMS *Queen Elizabeth*'s air group is built around the F-35B Lightning.
(MOD/CROWN COPYRIGHT)

BELOW: The RAF is integrating the 5th generation F-35B into its routine training exercises.
(MOD/CROWN COPYRIGHT)

Poseidon MRA1

The RAF's Kipper Fleet Reborn

ABOVE: Boeing's UK personnel are helping to support the RAF Poseidon MRA1 force while RAF personnel are being trained up.
(MOD/CROWN COPYRIGHT)

As first missions go, it was a gentle baptism of fire. The Russian corvette, the *Vasily Bykov,* had entered the North Sea and 120 Squadron was tasked with finding it. A Boeing Poseidon MRA1 was launched from the Squadron's temporary base at Kinloss Barracks in Moray on August 7, 2020, and in less than an hour the Russian ship was in view. For several hours, the RAF jet shadowed the *Vasily Bykov* before returning to its Scottish base.

A week later, 120 Squadron found itself called into action again in very different circumstances. Pitiful migrants were attempting to cross the English Channel in ever increasing numbers in inflatable boats. By early August, the Border Force had asked for military help to monitor the waterway between England and France. The first aircraft on patrol on August 10 was an Airbus A400M transport, which was alert as the national standby aircraft at RAF

RIGHT: The first UK Poseidon MRA1 flew for the first time in July 2019.
(MOD/CROWN COPYRIGHT)

Brize Norton, but its crew had little in the way of surveillance equipment except for binoculars. A more capable aircraft was needed, so on August 12 a Poseidon was launched from Kinloss to fly up and down the Channel.

The RAF was now back in the maritime patrol game after a 10-year capability gap. It was fitting that 120 Squadron flew its first missions from the former RAF Kinloss, which is now a British Army base, as this

was where the last Hawker Siddeley Nimrod MR2 served until the type's premature retirement in March 2010. The runway and other airport facilities were retained at Kinloss Barracks to allow it act in emergencies as a temporary operating site for nearby RAF Lossiemouth.

The renaissance of the Kipper Fleet, as the Nimrod Force (and before it RAF Coastal Command) had been nicknamed, had its origins in the November 2015 National Security Strategy and Strategic Defence and Security Review, which recognised the lack of maritime patrol aircraft was a key capability gap that needed to be addressed. Plans to buy nine Poseidon aircraft for the RAF were approved by Prime Minister David Cameron.

The formal title of the project is the UK Persistent Wide Area Surveillance – Maritime (PWAS-M), and it was needed to meet an "urgent anti-submarine-warfare-driven requirement". The target for an initial operational capability (IOC) of two aircraft was set for April 2020. It had to deliver aircraft with both anti-submarine warfare (ASW) and anti-surface warfare capabilities.

Procurement activity accelerated in March 2017 when the first contracts for production of aircraft for the United Kingdom were placed as

part of a batch of 17 aircraft for the US Navy. The delivery schedule envisaged all nine aircraft being handed over between the spring of 2020 and early 2022.

The RAF has a long history of maritime patrol operations stretching back to World War Two when Coastal Command played a key role in defeating Nazi U-boats during the Battle of the Atlantic. During the Cold War, RAF Nimrod crews regularly won plaudits for their anti-submarine warfare skills. RAF crews won the UK/Canada/New Zealand/Australia

Fincastle Trophy for ASW skills 18 times out of the 43 occasions it was held up to 2008.

Bringing the Poseidon into service requires different skills to those perfected by the old Nimrod community, with RAF officers involved in the Poseidon programme repeatedly telling audiences, "This is not a new Nimrod".

The P-8A boasts many of the traditional features of an MRA, including the ability to launch and control sonobuoys to find and monitor submarines and other »

ABOVE: RAF Lossiemouth's Typhoon fighters welcome the first Poseidon MRA1 to the skies over Moray in February 2020. (MOD/CROWN COPYRIGHT)

BELOW: The first RAF Poseidon MRA1 assumed temporary residence at the former RAF Kinloss while RAF Lossiemouth's runway was being upgraded. (MOD/CROWN COPYRIGHT)

ABOVE: RAF Poseidon MRA1s restored the UK maritime patrol capability that was lost by the scrapping the Nimrod MRA4 in 2010.
(MOD/CROWN COPYRIGHT)

RIGHT: Two Poseidon MRA1 units, 120 and 201 Squadrons, are now stood up at RAF Lossiemouth.
(MOD/CROWN COPYRIGHT)

underwater threats. It features an AN/APY-10 surface surveillance radar and a forward-looking infrared sensor turret and can be armed with Mk 54 Lightweight Hybrid Torpedoes (LHTs) and AGM-84 Harpoon II anti-ship missiles. The aircraft's mission systems are fully digital, allowing wide area surveillance and enhanced network connectivity with other air, land, and naval assets.

Two new RAF squadrons have been formed to operate the United Kingdom's Poseidon, the first stood up in April 2018. RAF Wing Commander James Hanson oversaw the formation of 120 Squadron, while the second unit, 201 Squadron, was stood up in August 2021. Both of

Poseidon Names
All the Poseidons will bear names linking them to the Moray area, RAF Lossiemouth or something of historic significance to the RAF maritime patrol community.
ZP801 Pride of Moray
ZP802 City of Elgin
ZP803 Terence Bulloch
ZP804 Spirit of Reykjavik
ZP805 Fulmar
ZP806 Guernsey's Reply
ZP807 William Barker VC
ZP808 not yet named
ZP809 not yet named

these units operated the Nimrod MR2 before the aircraft was retired from service and have a strong tradition of maritime patrol duties stretching back to Coastal Command days.

The first RAF frontline crews and maintenance personnel entered training at the US Navy Poseidon school house at Naval Air Station (NAS) Jacksonville in Florida in January 2019. Thirty-eight RAF personnel of 120 Squadron arrived in the US to begin operational conversion training. This involved the first fully

formed UK crew to undergo training in the US, with previous RAF personnel being trained at NAS Jacksonville as individuals seconded to US Navy units under Project Seedcorn to gain experience of the Poseidon. This was initiated after the scrapping of the Nimrod MR2 and its successor, the Nimrod MRA4, in a bid to retain vital maritime patrol skills and expertise in the RAF by posting personnel to the US Navy, Royal Australia Air Force, Royal New Zealand Air Force and Royal Canadian Air Force.

Poseidon MRA1	
In service:	2020 to date
Used by:	Royal Air Force
Manufacturer:	Boeing
Produced:	2009 onwards
Number built:	Nine
Specifications	
Powerplant:	Two × CFM56-7B27A turbofans
Length:	39.47m (129ft 5in)
Wingspan:	37.64m (123ft 6in)
Height:	12.83m (42ft 1in)
Max take-off weight:	85,820kg (189,200lb)
Maximum speed:	907km/h (490kts)
Combat range:	2,222km (1,200nm)
Crew:	Nine
Avionics	
Raytheon APY-10 multi-mission surface search radar AN/APS-154 Advanced Airborne Sensor	
Armament	
AGM-84 Harpoon, Mark 54 torpedo, mines, depth charges and possibly the High Altitude Anti-Submarine Warfare Weapon Capability (HAAWC) system.	

airbase. Eventually the aim is to have 18 Poseidon crews to operate its nine aircraft when full operation capability is declared in 2024. Five crews had been trained by early 2022.

The start of UK Poseidon operational conversion training was a major milestone in the RAF programme to regenerate a maritime patrol aircraft capability, running in parallel with assembly work starting on the first UK aircraft. The first two UK Poseidons operated from Kinloss Barracks until runway repairs at RAF Lossiemouth were completed in October 2020, which allowed them to move to their permanent home.

The first UK Poseidon, ZP801, now named *Pride of Moray*, was handed over to the RAF in October 2019 and it flew to Kinloss on February 4, 2020.

Strategic Facility

The RAF Poseidon programme includes not just the procurement of the aircraft but also encompasses the training for aircrew and maintenance personnel, as well as support infrastructure at RAF Lossiemouth.

This project is part of the wider Lossiemouth Development Plan which is being managed by the UK Defence Infrastructure Organisation (DIO). The new Poseidon Strategic Facility will include a tactical operations centre, facilities for an operational conversion unit, squadron accommodation, training, and simulation facilities and a three-bay aircraft hangar.

The dedicated P-8A simulation centre will house simulators that include two flight deck crew operational flight trainers (OFTs) and weapons tactics trainers (WTTs) to train rear-cabin mission crew.

The RAF's Kipper Fleet is now firmly back in business and the UK's maritime patrol capability gap that opened with the retirement of Nimrod MR2 in 2010 is now being closed. For the foreseeable future, the RAF's new Lord of the Sea will be patrolling around Britain's coasts.

LEFT: The historic 120 Squadron returned to the RAF frontline in 2018 to be the first Poseidon unit.
(MOD/CROWN COPYRIGHT)

BELOW: Training up aircrew to fly the Poseidon MRA1 is now a top priority for the RAF.
(MOD/CROWN COPYRIGHT)

The ramp-up of the UK Poseidon training effort initially took place within the US Navy conversion organisation at NAS Jacksonville before the Poseidon training organisation moved to the UK in late 2021, following the installation of a set of simulators at the future Poseidon main operating base at RAF Lossiemouth. A training flight within the UK Intelligence, Surveillance, Target Acquisition and Reconnaissance (ISTAR) training unit, 54 Squadron, has been set up to run the training organisation at the Scottish

Wedgetail AEW1

The RAF Renews its Airborne Early Warning Force

The United Kingdom fielded the world's first-ever operational early warning radar network – Chain Home – more than 80 years ago. Soon after it became operational in the late 1930s it played a critical role in the defeat of the Nazi Luftwaffe in the Battle of Britain and since then the Royal Air Force has recognised the critical strategic and operational importance of maintaining situational awareness in the air domain.

Technology has moved on since the 1940s when the network comprised ground-based radars that relied on cathode ray tubes and mechanically rotating antenna. Today the RAF is investing in a new airborne early warning and control (AEW&C) system that is built around an active electronically scanned array (AESA) radar. The new Boeing E-7 or Wedgetail AEW1 system will be the first RAF AEW&C platform to employ this technology. It will replace the veteran Boeing E-3D, designated

Sentry AEW1s, which served between 1991 and 2021.

Although the new technology will provide a dramatic leap in capability for the service, the cost of the programme came under scrutiny in the March 2021 UK Integrated Review of Security, Defence, Development and Foreign Policy, which resulted in a cut in the number of Wedgetail aircraft being purchased from five to three.

The previous defence review, released in 2010, had opted to skip around a cycle of upgrades to the UK E-3D fleet, leaving them out of step with their US, French and NATO counterparts that were now fielding radar enhancements and other system upgrades. The cost of ownership of the RAF E-3D fleet was also becoming an issue. In 2016 the aircraft had to be grounded after an electrical fire that resulted in an expensive rewiring exercise being ordered. With these issues becoming more apparent in 2017, the RAF leadership began pushing for a more radical solution. They persuaded the Ministry of Defence to cancel the proposed E-3D upgrade and plough the savings into buying a new solution.

The Wedgetail and its Northrop Grumman Multi-role Electronically Scanned Array (MESA) radar also offered significant growth potential. This move culminated in an announcement in October 2018 by the then-defence secretary Gavin Williamson that he had selected the Wedgetail AEW&C system and a £1.5bn contract for five Wedgetail

aircraft was placed with Boeing the following March.

The solution selected by the UK to meet its requirement was the Australian variant of the Boeing 737 AEW&C. The US defence giant had been working with the Royal Australian Air Force (RAAF) during the 1990s to field an AEW&C platform with an AESA radar rather than a mechanically rotated radar.

The USAF has still not ordered a replacement for its E-3s, so the

737 AEW&C remains a purely commercial product for export markets, managed by the US-based Boeing Defense, Space and Security. This company also remains responsible for the configuration management or design authority control of the system for its international customers.

The UK has ordered aircraft in a similar configuration to the Australian platforms to reduce the amount of development work »

ABOVE: The first Boeing 737 airframe has arrived in the UK to be modified into the first RAF Wedgetail AEW1. (BOEING UK)

BELOW: The passenger seats and other internal fittings have been removed to make way for the Wedgetail mission system. (BOEING UK)

required. However, some airframe and aircraft systems are different because Boeing has changed components on its 737NG/ER production line since the aircraft were originally ordered by Australia in the 1990s.

After being contracted by the UK in 2019, Boeing activated the supply chain to purchase the airframes and other components. It also began negotiating with potential partners in the UK to establish a conversion facility, which followed the model used in Turkey and South Korea.

Boeing acquired two pre-owned 737NG airframes from the commercial sector early in 2020 and then selected slots for new-build airframes on its production line in Renton, Washington. Boeing opted in May 2020 for US company STS Aviation Services to conduct the conversion work in the UK.

In October 2019, the Florida-based company had purchased the former Monarch aircraft maintenance operation at Birmingham Airport in the UK, which was selected to be the site for the conversion of all the RAF Wedgetails.

The conversion work involves stripping out the airliner's interior to enable the installation of the Wedgetail mission system and crew stations. To support the MESA antenna and its protective housing, the rear fuselage must be reinforced to carry the additional weight. The first new fuselage sections arrived at STS Aviation's Birmingham site in November 2020 and the first 'green' 737NG arrived three months later. Boeing disclosed in 2021 that the first radar will be shipped to Birmingham in 2022 to be installed in the first airframe. The new-build third UK Wedgetail made its first flight from

Boeing's Renton site on March 15, 2022, prior to delivery to Birmingham.

As part of its global supply chain, Boeing selected the UK arm of Leonardo to deliver an integrated Defensive Aids System (DAS) for the UK Wedgetails, based on the latest iteration of the company's Electronic Warfare Suite Controller (EWSC), which is also used by the RAAF on its Wedgetail fleet. Thales UK, under a subcontract from Leonardo, will provide its Elix-IR Threat Warning System and Vicon XF Intelligent Countermeasures Dispensing System.

Unlike previous 737 AEW&C projects, all ground and flight trials will take place in the UK, with the first flight scheduled for mid-2023. After initial Boeing-run trials, the first aircraft will be delivered to its new home at RAF Lossiemouth by the end of 2023.

RAF sources say the first Wedgetail aircraft has a target in-service date of 2023, and the service anticipates the second aircraft to be delivered in 2024. "The third E-7 Wedgetail aircraft is likely to be delivered in 2025," said the source. "However the programme is being reviewed following the Integrated Review decision to reduce the number of airframes, including delivery dates, and we're not able to confirm these at this time." RAF officers say the cancellation of the fourth and fifth aircraft has saved the service several hundred million pounds in procurement and support costs but it has also left the MoD having to restructure other aspects of the Wedgetail programme.

The RAF unit destined to operate the Wedgetail is 8 Squadron which, fittingly, flew the old Shackleton AEW2 between 1972 and 1991 at RAF Lossiemouth. In a return to the old Cold War role in the North Atlantic

theatre of operations, the Wedgetail unit will reform at RAF Lossiemouth where it will be well placed to support the interception of Russian aircraft in this strategic region.

The RAF has already begun preparing to transition from the E-3D to the Wedgetail. It has established the Airborne Early Warning Seedcorn programme with Australia at its E-7A base at RAAF Williamtown, New South Wales. There are approximately 20 personnel fully integrated in the RAAF E-7 programme, including pilots, mission crew and groundcrew. These personnel will form the cadre of the new 8 Squadron when it eventually reforms at RAF Lossiemouth and begins trials on the first Wedgetail, before beginning to train up more personnel for the unit.

Under current plans the Wedgetail squadron will share the newly built Strategic Facility at RAF Lossiemouth, which is home to the RAF's newly delivered Boeing Poseidon MRA1 maritime patrol aircraft fleet. As they share a similar airframe, the UK Poseidon and Wedgetail fleets are being treated as a single fleet for many support aspects. Both aircraft types will undergo routine intermediate-level maintenance inside the Strategic Facility's three hangar bays.

It seems likely that the RAF will use its Wedgetails in the same way as its E-3Ds: to provide command and control in the air, land and maritime domains, as well as airborne early warning of hostile air and missile attacks.

The reduced airframe numbers increase the importance of high-quality virtual training environments. It is also expected that 8 Squadron will continue to provide the UK's contribution to the NATO AEW&C and will coordinate operations in support of NATO and elsewhere. RAF sources said they expected these arrangements will need to be revised to accommodate the UK's smaller Wedgetail fleet.

The Wedgetail will provide the RAF with a quantum leap in airborne early warning capability, with its powerful AESA radar that outstrips the capabilities of the old rotating radar on the E-3D. Moreover, its digital antenna can be upgraded via software changes at a fraction of the cost of upgrading a mechanical radar.

Tempest Future Combat Air System

The Next Generation of RAF Airpower

In July 2018, the then UK defence secretary, Gavin Williamson, strode into the BAE Systems pavilion at the Farnborough Air Show to unveil a full-size model of the company's proposed Tempest combat aircraft.

The ebullient Williamson then announced the UK Government's commitment to buy a next generation of combat air systems from BAE Systems and its three major industry partners — Rolls-Royce, MBDA and Leonardo. International partners would be invited to join the UK-led programme, said Williamson.

For frequent visitors to the Farnborough Air Show this was a remarkable event. Not only was Williamson committing to replace the UK's existing fleet of Eurofighter Typhoon FGR4 jets with a new manned aircraft, but he was putting a marker in the ground to say that the UK would lead this effort. Not since 1960 had the UK launched a national programme to build a fast

BELOW: Tempest is made up of several elements, including a manned platform, guided weapons, and unmanned aerial vehicles.
(BAE SYSTEMS)

jet combat aircraft, which took the shape of the Hawker Siddeley Harrier Jump Jet. With his bullish statement, Williamson was reversing nearly 60 years of UK military aircraft procurement orthodoxy, which had said that the country did not have the financial and technical resources or political will to build its own fast jets.

"We have been a world leader in the combat air sector for a century," said Williamson at Farnborough, while standing in front of the model Tempest, "with an enviable array of skills and technology, and [our Combat Air] Strategy makes clear that we are determined to make sure it stays that way."

Not surprisingly, the stark reality of what Williamson was saying took a while to sink in but when it did it was welcomed as a refreshing change of direction from the UK Government, which up to then had seemed wedded to the mantra of 'value for money' and 'off the shelf' purchases of foreign aircraft. Phrases such as "sovereign capability", being "masters of our own destiny" and "protecting the UK defence industrial base" were now being used by UK ministers and industry executives for the first time in decades.

Four years on from the excitement of the unveiling of the Tempest model, the world has changed. Despite the inevitable hype around the unveiling of the Tempest model at the Farnborough Air Show, in the UK Government's Combat Air

Strategy document published on the day of Williamson's announcement it became very clear that Tempest was not a finished design of an aircraft about to go into production but the name of an overarching project to design, build, deliver and sustain a future combat air platform and all its supporting weapons, sensors, partnered unmanned systems, communications networks, logistic support and other infrastructure. The plan is to bring the first of the new aircraft into service by 2035 so all the

Royal Air Force's Typhoons can be retired by 2040.

There are two key milestones to meet over the next five years. As a result of the March 2021 Integrated Review of Security, Defence, Development and Foreign Policy, the Tempest project has moved into what used to be known as 'assessment phase' work. This is now moving towards building a flying demonstrator aircraft and support systems, such as precision guided munitions and advanced sensors, »

ABOVE: Tempest will be built at BAE Systems' Warton site in Lancashire. (BAE SYSTEMS)

BELOW: Work on a flying demonstrator of Tempest is the next phase of the project. (BAE SYSTEMS)

ABOVE: Robots will be used extensively in the manufacture of Tempest. (BAE SYSTEMS)

BELOW: The sun will not set on manned combat aircraft when Tempest enters service. (BAE SYSTEMS)

as well as partnered unmanned aerial vehicles or 'unmanned wingmen'. These technologies are expected to be developed as integral elements of the Tempest system in parallel with the core air vehicle rather than be bolted on at a later date.

Two organisations have been set up to run the effort to build the Tempest and they are often confused. The UK Ministry of Defence has set up its Combat Air Acquisition Programme, which is its overarching project name. It will eventually migrate into a procurement team, involving both the Ministry's London Main Building staff and its Defence Equipment & Support (DE&S)

organisation at Abbey Wood in Bristol, which will take over buying the aircraft once it is approved for production in 2025.

Until then the lead organisation is dubbed Team Tempest and it is tasked with eventually developing and building demonstrator aircraft, support weapons and other systems that will be offered up to the Ministry of Defence. Unusually, Team Tempest is a joint organisation made up of government, military, and industry bodies working together to develop the product and its technology.

The 2015 UK National Security Strategy and Strategic Defence and Security Review set aside £2bn for a

project dubbed the Future Combat Air System Technology Initiative (FCAS TI), which is to be spent up to 2025. Just under £10bn has been allocated to complete the project.

The early development work is being run by the Team Tempest organisation from an office building in Farnborough in Hampshire. On the government side, the lead organisation is the RAF's Rapid Capabilities Office, assisted by personnel from the Defence Science and Technology Laboratory (Dstl) and Defence Equipment & Support (DE&S). The industry effort involves four main partners: BAE Systems, engine supplier Rolls-Royce, the UK arm of the Italian electronic systems house Leonardo and European missile company MBDA.

The work of Team Tempest is organised by means of a series of streams that involve specific research projects. According to documents released by Team Tempest, there are four core work streams. The Joint Next Generation Concepting & Integrated Design activities involve the overarching system design. This is led by the RAF Rapid Capabilities Office and involves all four partner companies. The Next Generation Air Vehicle technical activities looks at possible designs for the manned and unmanned air platform components and it primarily involves BAE Systems and MDBA. Rolls-Royce is leading the Power Support and Thermal Signature work stream

LEFT: The UK has teamed up with Italy and Sweden to move the Tempest programme forward. (BAE SYSTEMS)

and work on Advanced Sensors and Communications is being led by Leonardo. These teams in turn are overseeing a further 60 smaller work streams or projects that are being run by the partner companies, sub contractors and academic institutions.

Although Team Tempest is headquartered in Farnborough, actual research and engineering activity takes place at other locations around the UK, mainly within the facilities of the partner companies. Team Tempest continues to expand its activities and during 2021 some 2,500 people were working on the project.

At the heart of the Tempest programme is the ambition to deliver a more effective combat air system for significantly less than previous generations of combat aircraft had cost

to build and operate. This involves looking at innovative manufacturing techniques and systems engineering to build Tempest in new ways. The recent US Air Force TX training aircraft programme that saw non-defence companies with expertise in advanced manufacturing technologies come to the fore was highlighted as an area BAE Systems is interested in.

A key to driving cost out of the Tempest programme is accelerating research, development, and production. By delivering the programme over a shorter time frame the fixed costs can be reduced and finished designs handed over for production at significantly lower cost.

It is not yet clear when a prototype or demonstrator air platform will actually fly, but spokesmen for

BAE Systems have said that the programme is not structured in a linear format built around an old-style flight test programme. As the programme moves forward, a number of the work streams running out to 2025/26 will involve the building of technology demonstrators.

During 2019, Italy and Sweden joined Team Tempest as industry partners working on "development of a joint acquisition roadmap, identifying technologies to spiral from Saab Gripen and Typhoon onto a new [system]," according to the UK Ministry of Defence. This work is the start of what it is hoped will grow into a fully fledged international procurement programme that will eventually see all three nations build and operate the new air system, or significant parts of it.

The crucial benefits of international partnership are that it brings added up-front government and industry investment to fund development work and an increased order book to drive down unit production costs. Developing a viable government and industrial construct to manage any future Tempest procurement is at the heart of the ongoing discussions with the Swedes and Italians.

There has been much speculation that Team Tempest could eventually be merged with the rival Franco-German and Spanish Future Combat Air Systems, but this talk seems to have been put on ice by the two groups of nations until they are further down the line and have proved they can actually deliver.

BELOW: For several years in the late 2030s Tempest and Typhoon will fly side by side in the RAF. (BAE SYSTEMS)

Protector RG1

Replacing the RAF Reaper Unmanned Aerial Vehicles

In August 2015, a Royal Air Force General Atomics MQ-9 Reaper unmanned aerial vehicle conducted the first-ever missile strike against British-born members of the Islamic State terrorist group inside the Syrian city of Raqqa. The political significance of the strike was reinforced by the fact that the then Prime Minister, David Cameron, personally announced the attack to Parliament. This was not something that could be made public in a low-key press release posted on the Ministry of Defence website.

A few weeks later, Cameron made clear that he wanted the RAF to maintain the capability to make similar strikes against terrorist safe havens long into the future. The RAF would be getting a new and enhanced UAV or drone capability that would remain in service for many decades.

On the other side of the Atlantic, the Aircraft Systems Group of the General Atomics (GA-ASI) company in California was already working on an improvement to its Reaper product that could meet the RAF's needs. The privately owned company which created first the iconic Predator and then the Reaper, had a long tradition of anticipating customer demand for product improvements and being ready to bring them online rapidly.

Since the USAF first used armed Predators in combat in Afghanistan in 2001, GA-ASI has experienced an insatiable demand for initially the platform and then for enhancements to its weapons, sensors, communications, engines, and airframes.

Just as the RAF was working up its requirements for a successor to the Reaper, General Atomics was investing its own money in its latest product, which was then known as the Certifiable Predator B (CPB). It eventually became the Sky Guardian in the US and Protector RG1 when developed for the UK. The aim was to evolve the existing Predator B, or MQ-9, design into a product that not only doubled range and weapon payload but also boasted enhanced

sensor performance and was certified to operate in civilian airspace.

To meet European airworthiness requirements, the whole privately funded certifiable project involves a root-and-branch re-engineering of the Predator B design to make it more robust and durable. The airframe is being strengthened with new materials to better withstand everything from lightning and bird strikes to tool drops during ground maintenance. Software enhancements will cover other areas including the flight control system.

These developments, which include an automatic take-off and landing capability, will also deliver significant performance improvements that, among other things, will help reduce accidents and double the new

product's fatigue life from 20,000 to 40,000 hours. GA-ASI is also working to develop a radar- and transponder-based sense-and-avoid system for the CPB: an essential prerequisite for operating in non-segregated airspace.

In November 2015, the UK's National Security Strategy and Strategic Defence and Security Review (SDSR) formally endorsed the Protector requirement, committing the UK to buy "more than 20 new Protector armed remotely piloted aircraft, more than doubling the number of the Reaper aircraft which they replace". The decision was quickly made that only the Certifiable Predator B would meet the RAF's requirements and a 'main gate' decision was made by the UK Ministry of Defence in April 2016 to begin contract negotiations with General Atomics.

A key attraction of the Certifiable Predator B for the RAF was not only its enhanced performance and payload, but the potential for the air vehicle to operate in the UK, Europe, and other locations where it would have to fly in controlled civilian airspace. Although the Reaper had performed superbly in Afghanistan, Iraq and Syria, there was little civilian air traffic in these countries and the RAF's future UAV needed to be able to operate in more congested environments. The intention was to home base the Protector force at RAF Waddington eventually, allowing the Protector to take part in training exercises with UK-based assets and potentially participate in homeland security and maritime security operations in support of civil authorities. »

It has become increasingly clear that the RAF Protector will have far more advanced capabilities than any other rival system, even the latest variants of the Reaper currently being procured by the USAF.

Progress moved fast. On November 17, 2016, the first prototype, YBC01, made its maiden flight and in December 2016 the UK Ministry of Defence announced it was making a £100 million investment in Protector development to fund the integration of unique UK weapons, including the MBDA Brimstone 2 missile and Raytheon Paveway IV dual-mode guided bomb as well as UK-specific X-Band SATCOM and a signals intelligence payload. The Protector will have nine weapons or stores pylons, including one on the fuselage centre line, compared to four on the Reaper.

The Protectors will also have a unique capability to allow operators to control the take-off and landing of air vehicles remotely over SATCOM via tablet computer without requiring a ground control station (GCS) cabin to be physically present at airfields. Current Predator and Reaper systems require a GCS cabin, supported by line-of-sight data links mounted on towers, to set up and operate a launch-and-recovery site. The SATCOM-based automatic take-off and landing could reduce the personnel

Protector RG1	
In service:	from 2024
Used by:	Royal Air Force
Manufacturer:	General Atomics
Produced:	from 2016
Number built:	16 on order
Specifications	
Length:	11.43m (37.5ft)
Wingspan:	24m (79ft)
Maximum take-off weight:	5669kg (12,500lbs)
Endurance:	40hrs +
Armament:	500lb Paveway IV laser-guided bombs and Brimstone 3 missiles.

requirements to support a Protector system by up to a half, increasing operational flexibility and reducing requirements to train pilots. This potentially increases the operational range of the system, allowing the use of austere bases to refuel air vehicles or divert them if technical problems emerge during missions.

Delivering the Protector programme is a complex activity that cuts across several lines of development, including test and evaluation, infrastructure, and training. The aim of the work is to ensure there is a smooth transition from Reaper and Protector and no gap in capability as the new system is introduced in early 2024. The original intention had been to bring the Protector into service by 2020 but budgetary pressures forced the RAF to stretch out the programme.

The project will include the building of what is called a 'strategic facility' that will house Protector operations at RAF Waddington in Lincolnshire. "This will include both operational and administrative functions," said an RAF source. "In addition, further accommodation will be built to house personnel involved. The strategic facility is intended to house seven ground control stations and seven simulators."

The first batch of Protector aircrew and engineers will be trained by GA-ASI at a bespoke training facility in North Dakota. This is intended to allow the RAF to develop the nucleus of the Protector Force. After the first tranche of personnel has been trained in North Dakota the training pipeline will switch to the RAF's Protector Operational Conversion Unit at RAF Waddington.

Once Protector is delivered, the RAF will have an operational level UAV system that can fly over the UK and out over the North Sea, English Channel and into the North Atlantic with an endurance of up to 40 hours. Protector could also potentially operate over the Baltic Sea from RAF Waddington.

When the range and SATCOM-based automatic take-off and landing capability are brought together, the operational flexibility of the Protector will surpass that of the current Reaper by several orders of magnitude. It could potentially fly from the UK to North Africa, be landed on a remote airstrip to be topped off with locally supplied fuel before heading on to its mission. This type of mission profile would involve only a handful of people having to deploy to a forward launch-and-recovery element.

The RAF hopes Protector will transform the United Kingdom's persistent surveillance and strike capabilities.

Apache AH2

The Army Air Corps New Attack Helicopter

BELOW: Army Air Corps pilots are now flying the new upgraded Apache AH2 from Wattisham Flying Station in Suffolk.
(MOD/CROWN COPYRIGHT)

The first of the Army Air Corps' (AAC) next generation attack helicopters formally entered service at Wattisham Flying Station in Suffolk in January 2022.

Designated the Boeing Apache AH2 in UK service, the new variant of the iconic Apache features improved weapons, sensors, and engines to make it more lethal and survivable on the battlefields of the future. The helicopters are similar in configuration to the US Army's AH-64E Version 6.0 but are known to their crews as the '64 Echo'.

Contracts were placed for the first 50 of the improved helicopters in

July 2016. Unlike the original British variant of the Apache, which were assembled by Westland Helicopters in Yeovil, Somerset, the majority of the work on the new variant is being carried out at the Boeing plant at Mesa in Arizona. The aim is to keep the British helicopters as similar to their US Army counterparts as possible to reduce manufacturing costs and allow future upgrades to be made efficiently.

The core fuselage, Longbow radar and many other smaller components from old AgustaWestland Apache AH1s are being recycled for use in the new helicopters. Known as the AH-64E Version 6, the new helicopter features more powerful General Electric T700-GE-701D engines, new transmissions, new composite rotor blades and improved landing gear. At the heart of the enhancements are new avionics and digital communications to allow the crew to access and share information rapidly with ground forces and other aircraft, including the facility for the AH-64E crew to control unmanned aerial vehicles flying as part of joint missions. A maritime mode is provided to enhance the performance of the

Longbow radar when operating over water. Embedded system-level diagnostics are incorporated in the new helicopter to allow ground crews to rapidly assess maintenance requirements between missions.

By July 2021 ten of the new helicopters had been airlifted to Wattisham from America on board RAF Boeing C-17 Globemaster airlifters. A cadre of instructor pilots has already started training with the US Army and once they have completed their conversion, they will come back to Wattisham to stand up an operational conversion unit. The plan is to have enough helicopters and trained crews to allow the first squadron from 3 Regiment AAC to be declared operational in mid-2022. Maintainers from the Royal Electrical and Mechanical Engineers are also undergoing training at Fort Eustis in Virginia, USA, to operate the new helicopters. All the old Apache AH1s are expected to have been retired by 2024 when all 50 of the new AH2s will be operational at Wattisham. A rolling programme of conversions to the new helicopter is currently underway within 3 Regiment AAC. Formal release to service of the AH2 was approved in ➤➤

ABOVE: The Army Air Corps has purchased 50 of the new AH-64E variants of the Apache. (MOD/CROWN COPYRIGHT)

late 2021 to allow frontline personnel to routinely train and operate the helicopter.

Once 3 Regiment AAC is fully converted and declared operational, then its sister unit at Wattisham, 4 Regiment AAC, will begin to train on the new helicopter. Until then, the latter is continuing to maintain high readiness to deploy on operations with the legacy AH1 helicopters to ensure there is no capability gap.

Once the new AH-64E squadrons are fully operational they will be assigned to the 1 Aviation Brigade Combat Team, which is part of the British Army's Global Response Force alongside 16 Air Assault Brigade. The two brigades will have units at high readiness to deploy to crisis zones around the world. Another important role will be to support the new Deep Reconnaissance Strike Brigade, which will have the mission of finding and attacking tank and artillery forces far behind enemy lines.

A 20-year agreement was signed in January 2022 between the Ministry of Defence with Boeing Defence UK to maintain and support the new fleet. This £287m deal will cover the

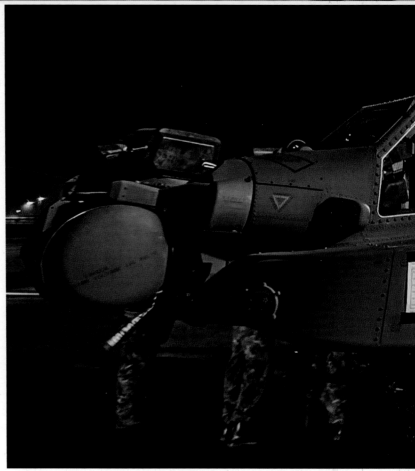

first period of the agreement and is in place until July 2025. The agreement will create more than 200 jobs in the UK, including 165 for the Army Aviation Centre at Middle Wallop in Hampshire and 45 at Wattisham Flying Station in Suffolk.

The Long-Term Training and Support Service (LTTSS) will progressively take over from the initial support and conversion training provided by the US government under Foreign Military Sale interim arrangements. It will eventually cover aircraft design organisation services, maintenance and logistics support, plus pilot, maintainer, and ground crew training.

During the ceremony in January 2022 to mark the Apache AH2's entry to service, Lieutenant Colonel Simon Wilsey, the commanding officer of 3 Regiment AAC, said: "The AH-64E Apache is a 21st century attack helicopter that is more lethal, agile, survivable, and integrated and will enhance the way the Army fights. It is a central part of Future Soldier and the British Army's warfighting capability. What is key to the AH-64E's improved capabilities is its ability to integrate with other ground and air assets, allowing us to share information so that we can find and strike the enemy before our forces are targeted themselves."

He continued: "Everyone in the Regiment – aircrew, engineers, and ground crew – is proud and excited to be at the forefront of bringing AH-64E into service. We have invested in the training of our people to maximise what we can do with such an advanced aircraft."

Warrant Officer Class 2 'O', an experienced pilot who is his squadron's flying instructor, said: "I'm very excited about flying the AH-64E. It is more agile, faster, more powerful and it is going to allow us to support ground forces and other air assets much better. The interoperability of this Apache is vastly improved. We have better communications systems, better sensors, the fire control radar has been enhanced. We've got lots more radios and Link 16, which allows us to share data quicker and with higher fidelity to ground forces, manned or unmanned aircraft."

Communications specialist Lance Corporal Dylan Jones works to programme the aircraft's computer systems with the information needed to conduct missions and he said new helicopter was a big improvement on the old AH1 variant.

"The new mission planning software on the AH-64E is far superior. It gives us a lot more accuracy in mission planning and gives the aircraft a lot more information, which makes it easier for aircrew to fly and fight the aircraft. It's exciting to be at the forefront of AH-64E transition, as we're setting the trend for other squadrons to follow as they change over."

BELOW: The first upgraded AH-64E Apache arrived at Wattisham Flying Station in Suffolk in November 2020 on board an RAF C-17 Globemaster aircraft.
(MOD/CROWN COPYRIGHT)

Chinook Extended Range

The RAF's Newest Version of the Iconic Heavy-lift Helicopter

The iconic Boeing Chinook heavy-lift helicopter has been operated by the Royal Air Force since 1981 and the service is in the midst of a major project to replace older airframes with new ones. Britain is the largest operator of the Boeing Chinook outside the US Army with 60 helicopters in service at the beginning of 2022.

Proven in battle and operated by the RAF in every major conflict since the Falklands War, the Chinook is a highly versatile aircraft. The helicopter can operate in a diverse range of environments, from deserts to the Arctic, and transport up to 55 personnel or 10 tonnes of cargo.

The RAF uses the Chinook to support the British Army, Royal Navy, and Royal Marines in a variety of roles, including air assault, logistical support, and disaster relief. They routinely operate from Royal Navy warships in support of amphibious landings and in the logistical re-supply role. Specially modified Chinooks are also dedicated to support UK Special Forces missions.

A £1.4bn contract to modernise the UK Chinook helicopter fleet over a ten- year period was announced in May 2021. The deal will see the RAF receive 14 of the latest version of the iconic heavy-lift helicopter. At the same time nine of the older air frames will be retired. The first of these, call

sign 'Bravo November', was retired in March 2022.

Bravo November had seen service in the 1982 Falklands war, 2003 Iraq war and in Afghanistan. During its 41-year career four pilots won the Distinguished Flying Cross at the controls of the helicopter. It famously survived an Exocet missile attack in 1982 and 21 years later landed the first troops ashore on the Al-Faw peninsula in southern Iraq in the first hours of the coalition invasion.

The retiring of Bravo November has left the RAF with 37 Chinook HC6A helicopters, the earliest of which were introduced in 1981 as the HC1 and were subsequently upgraded

BELOW: Flares are an essential part of the defensive aid suite used by RAF Chinook heavy-lift helicopters.
(MOD/CROWN COPYRIGHT)

Chinook HC6

Specifications	
Power plant:	Two Honeywell T55-L-714A turboshafts
Length:	30.14m (98ft 10½in)
Height:	5.77m (18ft 11in)
Speed:	296km/h (183mph)
Crew:	3 to 4
Capacity:	up to 55 troops or 10,000kg (22,000lb) of freight
Armament	
Two x 7.62mm M134 mini guns and one x 7.62mm M60D machine gun	

to HC2 and HC4 standards. These are similar in configuration to the US Army's CH-47D-standard. The RAF also has eight HC5 variants, which are similar to the US Army MH-47E-standard, and 14 HC6/6As which are comparable to the US Army CH-47F.

The 14 new H-47(ER) Chinooks that the UK will be getting are broadly similar to the MH-47G helicopter flown by the US Special Operations Command. The new British Chinooks will be Block 2 standard but will be fitted with some UK-specific avionics to ensure commonality with the

existing Chinook HC5/6/6A fleets. Once the last of the new helicopters have been delivered, the size of the UK fleet will shrink to 51 airframes.

With a top speed of 300km/h, the new H-47 Extended Range helicopters will have a raft of new capabilities, including an advanced digital cockpit, a modernised airframe to increase stability and improve survivability and a digital automatic flight control system to allow pilots to hover in areas of limited visibility.

The 14 aircraft will be purchased from the US via a Foreign Military Sales agreement that includes development and manufacture over the next decade. Deliveries are scheduled to start in 2026. The new helicopters will be based at RAF Odiham in Hampshire, the home of the RAF Chinook fleet.

LEFT: 7 Squadron's Chinooks were deployed in Afghanistan from 2001 onwards to support the UK Special Forces' contingent in the central Asian country.
(MOD/CROWN COPYRIGHT)

BELOW: The RAF Chinook fleet has been flying the British Army into battle for nearly 40 years.
(MOD/CROWN COPYRIGHT)

RIGHT: A mass take-off of Wildcat AH1s from RNAS Yeovilton in Somerset, the main operating base of all the UK's Wildcat helicopters.
(MOD/CROWN COPYRIGHT)

Wildcat AH1

Enhancing the British Army Battlefield Surveillance Helicopters

BELOW: The Army Air Corps is keen to fit a Sea Spray radar to its Wildcat AH1s to enhance their surveillance capabilities.
(TIM RIPLEY)

The Army Air Corps' (AAC) AgustaWestland Wildcat AH1 battlefield surveillance helicopters are benefiting from new network and surveillance technologies and consideration is being given to fitting them with the Sea Spray radars used by the Royal Navy maritime HMA2 variants of the helicopters.

A senior AAC officer said the flight trials during 2021 using Wildcat HMA2s in the overland role has been "very positive" and this would feed into a wider initiative to enhance surveillance and network technologies employed on the British Army's Wildcat AH1s.

The trials involved groups of Wildcats operating over Salisbury Plain training area in Wiltshire with a radar-equipped HMA2 flying at high altitude to look for targets using its Sea Spray radar's Ground Moving Target Indicator (GMTI) and Synthetic Aperture Radar (SAR) modes. "We would then send a Wildcat AH1 down to positively identify targets using its thermal imaging camera," said an AAC pilot involved in the trials.

The Royal Navy purchased its Wildcat HMA2 with legacy Sea Spray radar fitted as standard, but the AAC's Wildcat AH1s were not fitted with the radar as a cost-saving measure. Installing the radar in the ACC helicopters was described by the AAC officer as "relatively low risk" because the legacy Sea Spray is already integrated on the Royal Navy helicopters and would only require minor engineer modifications to physically fit the new one. The updated Sea Spray V2 variant is being proposed for the project, which has improved performance because of new hardware and software, according to industry sources.

Fitting the Sea Spray V2 radar is part of an on-going effort to enhance the capabilities on the AAC's Wildcat. A programme is soon to deliver Link 16 data links, which will for the first time allow AAC helicopters to merge an air and ground picture – generated via the British Army's Bowman radio system – on single map display.

Merlin HM2 Crowsnest

A New Airborne Early Warning System for the Royal Navy's Aircraft Carriers

The Royal Navy's AgustaWestland Merlin HM2 Crowsnest Airborne Surveillance and Control (ASaC) helicopter formally entered service with 820 Naval Air Squadron in March 2021 ahead of its deployment on HMS *Queen Elizabeth* for the Carrier Strike Group 21 cruise to the Far East.

The distinctive-looking helicopter has a large radar dome or 'bag' that sticks out from its fuselage, earning the aircraft the affectionate nickname of 'baggers'. The new generation of 'baggers' take on the mantle of the Royal Navy's veteran Sea Kings, which until 2018 flew with 849 Naval Air Squadron.

The ASaC Merlin's new mission systems and Searchwater 2000 radars are provided by Thales Group and the equipment has been installed by aerospace company Leonardo in Yeovil, Somerset, overseen by prime contractor Lockheed Martin. Ten sets of Crowsnest equipment are being purchased. They are designed to be rapidly installed on Merlin helicopters according to operational requirements.

Each helicopter has a crew of three: two observers (mission and tactical specialists) and one pilot. The helicopters will fly high above the carrier strike group so they can see well beyond the horizon to understand, and react to any air

or surface threats. They can also function as a control centre for strike operations between the carrier and the ship's Lockheed Martin F-35B Lightning jets.

The Crowsnest project has been plagued by technical problems, though, and it missed its 2019 target to enter service. The three Crowsnest Merlins that took part in the Carrier

Strike Group 21 deployment were all pre-Initial Operational Capability (IOC) equipment sets that were not fully certified. Full IOC was originally scheduled for September 2021, but the Ministry of Defence has not yet formally declared that the system has met this milestone. Full Operational Capability is now scheduled for May 2023.

ABOVE: The first Crowsnest variant of the Merlin HM2 maritime helicopter joined *HMS Queen Elizabeth* for her cruise to the Far East in 2021. (MOD/CROWN COPYRIGHT)

LEFT: A Crowsnest variant of the Merlin HM2 maritime helicopter during trials to evaluate its airborne early warning system. (LOCKHEED MARTIN)

Watchkeeper WK450

The British Army's Eye in the Sky

ABOVE: The Watchkeeper is dependent on runways or grass airstrips to get airborne. (MOD/CROWN COPYRIGHT)

BELOW: The Watchkeeper Tactical Unmanned Aerial Vehicle is the Royal Artillery's eye in the sky (TIM RIPLEY)

The British Army aims to have the first enhancements to its Thales Watchkeeper WK450 Tactical Unmanned Aerial Vehicle (TUAV) system ready by 2026. Its Watchkeeper Mid-life Extension (MLE) project passed initial approvals in August 2021, with initial operating capability planned for 2026 and full operating capability for 2027.

Although the March 2021 Defence Command Paper confirmed that the British Army would "retain and upgrade Watchkeeper", it now appears that the focus of the project is on replacing obsolete components rather than adding new capabilities such as new sensors or weapons.

"The primary work for the system will be on the ground control station," said a senior British Army source. "The MLE looks to modularise the critical items to enable future upgrades and create a more robust system when deployed. There will be improvements to the capability through an up-to-date operating system, including wider systems integration."

The MLE project is overseen by the British Army's land Intelligence, Surveillance, Target Acquisition and Reconnaissance (ISTAR) programme office.

A British Army spokesperson said, "Watchkeeper is an ISTAR platform which increases situational awareness for soldiers on the ground and can direct fire from other platforms. The exact nature of the Mid-life Extension and upgrades that may or may not be applied alongside it are being considered as part of the approvals process, which is ongoing."

Watchkeeper has a vital role in providing ISTAR support for British Army battlegroups, brigades, and divisional-sized formations. Its long and tortuous procurement process has meant that several main subsystems and components, such as the ground segment, are nearing obsolescence and therefore need to be replaced.

Obsolescence management appears to have a greater priority than adding new sensors or weapons to the TUAV. Israeli versions of the Elbit Hermes 450, on which the Watchkeeper air frame design is based, are believed to be armed. It appears that the installation of weapons on the Watchkeeper will have to wait until other work has been completed.

L-159E Honey Badger

New Red Air Aggressors

Royal Air Force fighter pilots will face a new adversary when conducting combat training following the signing of a contract for the interim provision of a Red Air 'aggressor' service.

Known as the Interim Red Air Aggressor Training Service (IRAATS), from July 1, 2022 the six-year contract with Draken Europe will see RAF fighter squadrons conducting training against fighter jets, replicating the tactics, techniques and procedures of potential adversaries.

The new service will use the Czech-made Aero L-159E Honey Badger, a military aircraft flown to military standards by experienced ex-military fast jet pilots regulated by the Civil Aviation Authority.

A simulated airborne threat was previously provided by the RAF's old Hawk T1, the retirement of which was announced last year. The L-159E delivers a capability enhancement over the Hawk through increased endurance, an air-to-air radar and a radar warning receiver.

"This exciting new capability increases the quality of operational training," said Air Commodore Ian Townsend, the RAF Senior Responsible Owner for the project. "By improving the currency, capability and survivability in combat of our Lightning and Typhoon fighter pilots we will enhance the potency of the UK's Combat Air capability. The contract was delivered through competition, from inception to contract signature, in an exceptionally short timescale of only six months. It is timely, affordable, deliverable and provides the UK with excellent value for money."

This is the first such contract for 'medium to fast' air capability placed in the UK, although a similar service is currently being delivered by Draken International to the United States Air Force.

The contract was placed in March 2022 and is for three years, starting on July 1, with options for up to a further three years. The contract will create up to 28 additional jobs in the aviation industry and will contribute towards the development of Teesside International Airport where the L-159Es will be co-located with Draken's existing Dassault 20 Falcon aircraft fleet. In September 2020, Draken International purchased Cobham Aviation Services, which previously operated the Falcon aircraft.

A replacement capability will in due course be provided by the Next Generation Operational Training (NGOT) programme.

BELOW: Aero L-159E aircraft operated by Draken International at Leeuwarden Air Base in the Netherlands in July 2017.
(GERARD VAN DER SCHAAF)

RQ-20 Puma and Wasp III

The Royal Navy Goes Unmanned

Royal Navy personnel have begun flying mini unmanned aerial vehicles (UAV) from an airfield in Cornwall as part of the service's experimentation drive.

The AeroVironment RQ-20 Puma and Wasp III UAV systems were purchased off the shelf for use by the Royal Navy's UAV experimental unit, 700X Naval Air Squadron (NAS).

These UAVs are being assessed for their suitability and applicability for use at sea and ashore by the Royal Navy and Royal Marines. This effort will involve a variety of different environments and situations.

700X Squadron is home based at RNAS Culdrose in Cornwall and uses the nearby Predannack diversion airfield for its flying operations.

A team of its UAV operators travelled to the manufacturer's facility in Huntsville, Alabama, to receive training ahead of the standing up of UK operations at Predannack Airfield. A handful of each system was purchased for the experiment.

The Squadron's commanding officer, Lieutenant Commander Justin Matthews, said in a statement that the unit is looking forward to putting the new-found skills into action in the UK. "Whilst learning the fundamentals of the Puma and Wasp air systems, we have developed an understanding of the tactical applications for both the Royal Navy and Royal Marines which we will progress now that we have returned to the UK," he said. "Once we gain more experience, then 700X NAS will progress to taking part in exercises in the UK for both maritime and land [environments]."

700X Squadron stood up in 2014 to administer teams of operators for the leased Boeing Scan Eagle UAV. Since this system was withdrawn from use by the Royal Navy on cost grounds, the Squadron has taken the lead in experimenting with other UAVs.

The Royal Navy wants to accelerate its use of unmanned platforms, including looking at the installation of an electromagnetic catapult and arrestor technology to its Queen Elizabeth-class aircraft carriers. This would potentially allow the Crowsnest-equipped early warning AgustaWestland Merlin helicopters to be replaced by an unmanned aerial vehicle.

BELOW: A Puma drone is launched from a Royal Navy warship in the Arabian Gulf by a member of 700X Naval Air Squadron.
(MOD/CROWN COPYRIGHT)

Dassault 900LX

Replacing the Classic BAe 146

The RAF's four veteran BAe 146 Command Support Air Transport (CSAT) aircraft were replaced by two Dassault 900LX aircraft on March 31, 2022. These new aircraft are flown and supported by a mix of civilian contractors and military personnel from 32 (The Royal) Squadron.

The £80m contract with Bristol-based Centreline to provide and operate the aircraft was announced in February 2022 and includes the purchase of two Dassault 900LX aircraft with two years of initial support, plus three optional extra years if required. Under Phase 1 of the project the new aircraft will be

ministers and senior military officers around the world. During the wars in Iraq, Afghanistan, and Libya the aircraft was used around the Middle East, flying cargo and personnel to remote locations as well as evacuating numerous casualties. The aircraft were fitted with defensive aid suites for protection. Two cargo-configured C3 variants were purchased in 2012 to augment this activity.

After nearly four decades of service, two BAe 146 aircraft are being preserved at the British Airliner Collection at Duxford in Cambridgeshire and the South Wales Aviation Museum at St Athan in the Vale of Glamorgan. A civilian operator has bought the remaining two aircraft.

ABOVE: The Falcon 900LX has replaced the veteran BAe 146 in 32 (The Royal) Squadron. (MOD/CROWN COPYRIGHT)

LEFT: Two Falcon 900LX will be operated initially by civilian crews until RAF personnel are trained up to fly the aircraft. (MOD/CROWN COPYRIGHT)

BELOW: A Royal Air Force BAe146 C3 at Camp Bastion in Afghanistan as a sandstorm looms in the background. (MOD/CROWN COPYRIGHT)

owned by the Ministry of Defence but operated on the Civil Aircraft Register, initially by contractor-provided civilian pilots. Phase 1 also includes the training of military pilots and cabin crew and the use of service personnel to complement the civilian pilots.

This will be followed by a separate competitive procurement that could see the embodiment of military modifications on the aircraft, including a defensive aid suite. It could also see the provision of in-service support utilising military personnel in the operation of the aircraft, with an associated transfer of aircraft to the Military Aircraft Register.

Two BAe 146 C2s entered service in 1986 with what was then The Queen's Flight and saw extensive service flying the Royal Family, government

Hawk T1/T2

Keeping the Hawk Flying

The UK Ministry of Defence is investing £695 million over the next 11 years to provide in-service support to the Royal Air Force's fleet of BAE Systems Hawk T2 training aircraft and the Hawker Siddeley Hawk T1 jets flown by the Red Arrows.

This will support hundreds of jobs at RAF Valley in Anglesey, North Wales, which is home to a fleet of 28 Hawk T2 jets. These aircraft are a vital training asset to deliver fast jet training and they form a key part of the UK Military Flying Training System (MFTS).

The Hawk Integrated Support Solution comprises two separate contracts placed by the Ministry of Defence's procurement arm, Defence Equipment and Support (DE&S). The Hawk contract with BAE Systems (BAES), valued at £590m, will cover all Hawk T2 airframe support elements. In addition, a separate £105m contract for engine support has been placed with Rolls-Royce.

"This is a major milestone for MFTS and the culmination of many months of hard work from the team at DE&S," said Air Vice-Marshal Simon Ellard, Director Combat Air at DE&S. "Through this investment, we will continue to train our student pilots to become the best in the business. The announcement represents excellent news for Anglesey, our workforce, and for sustaining our core business of delivering world class training to our future fighter pilots. The Hawk T2 is a fantastic platform to train our Typhoon and Lightning pilots on, readying them for the demands of the frontline; this level of ongoing investment ensures UK Defence will retain our military edge within the contested air environment."

The new contract will initially secure more than 500 highly skilled jobs working for BAES and its maintenance partner Babcock International. These will be mainly based at RAF Valley, with a small number of BAES support roles located at other UK sites.

Shadow R2

Protecting the RAF's Versatile Surveillance Aircraft

A major upgrade of the RAF Beechcraft Shadow R2 surveillance aircraft fleet is now underway after Raytheon UK received a £110m contract for the work in November 2021.

The new upgrade will see the eight Shadow R2 aircraft fitted with Leonardo Miysis Directed Infrared Countermeasure (DIRCM) suites to enhance their ability to defend themselves and operate in unfriendly airspace. The upgrade work is to be conducted at the Raytheon's site at Broughton in Flintshire, North Wales, where support work on the RAF Shadow fleet is carried out.

Based at RAF Waddington in Lincolnshire and flown by 14 Squadron, the Shadow R1 forms a key part of the RAF's Intelligence, Surveillance, Target Acquisition and Reconnaissance (ISTAR) force. It gathers intelligence via its high-definition electro-optical and electronic sensors. Once the data has been gathered, satellite communication links enable the information to be assessed while the aircraft is airborne during a mission.

"This investment will enable the Shadow fleet to be increased in size and equipped with the latest technology, providing a key capability as part of the RAF's next generation Air Force," said Group Captain Shaun Gee, Shadow

Programme Senior Responsible Owner. "It is expected the first upgraded aircraft will be delivered to the RAF in June 2023, with delivery of the eighth Shadow R2 aircraft before the end of 2025."

The original Shadow R1 variant entered service in 2007 at the height of the Afghanistan war and was used extensively to support Special Forces operations in the country. In the 2015 defence review an upgrade to the new R2 configuration was approved,

which included improvements to the aircraft's sensors and communications and an expansion of the fleet from five to eight.

The aircraft have since seen action in Iraq and Syria from 2014, to support counter-terrorist operations. In August 2020, Shadow aircraft were deployed to patrol the English Channel in support of efforts by the UK Border Force to intercept migrants trying to cross the waterway in small boats.

ABOVE: RAF Shadow R2 ISTAR aircraft are receiving a new defensive aid suite to enhance their protection in high-threat environments.
(MOD/CROWN COPYRIGHT)

LEFT: The RAF developed the Shadow R1 to give the UK a similar capability as the US Air Force has in its MC-12 Liberty ISTAR aircraft that have electro-optical sensors and signals intelligence gathering capabilities.
(RHL IMAGES)

New Medium Helicopter

Britain's New Military Helicopter

performance and reliability. A 2014 upgrade gave the Puma new engines, transmission, and other systems but its 1960s design could not go on forever.

Helicopter technology has moved on dramatically since then and the RAF is keen to acquire a more modern machine that has a lower cost of ownership. The other helicopters under the umbrella of the NMH project are supplied and supported by private contractors and the Ministry of Defence thinks it can find economies by simplifying those arrangements.

A prior information notice was published by the Ministry of Defence in November 2021, which outlined the scope of the project and the intention to carry out early engagement with potential suppliers. This will lead to a competition, and the Ministry indicated that it anticipated 36 to 44 new helicopters would be procured, as well as two cockpit flight simulators and one cabin simulator. The £1bn procurement effort is anticipated to run from October 2023 until October 2028, and as well as the provision of aircraft would include air and ground crew training as well as technical support and maintenance.

The NMH programme has attracted interest from several vendors. Possible contenders and their helicopters include Boeing's MH-139 Grey Wolf and Bell's 525 Relentless. Airbus is likely to offer its H175, NH90 and/or the H225M

ABOVE: Leonardo is offering its AW189 as its solution to the UK's New Medium Helicopter project. (LEONARDO)

The starting gun on a competition to provide the British Armed Services with replacement medium helicopters was fired in the March 2021 Integrated Review of Security, Defence, Development and Foreign Policy.

This confirmed the launch of the New Medium Helicopter (NMH) project to replace the Royal Air Force's Eurocopter Puma HC2 helicopters by 2025, as well as the Bell Griffin HAR2s, Bell 212s and Airbus Dauphins used by the RAF and Army Air Corps in a variety of roles.

The veteran Puma first entered service in 1971 and the helicopter provided stalwart service in several operational theatres. Crews valued its

RIGHT: The legacy Puma HC1 entered service with the RAF in 1971 and has seen stalwart service around the world since. (MOD/CROWN COPYRIGHT)

helicopters, while Lockheed Martin/ Sikorsky is offering the latest variants of UH-60 Black Hawk and, separate from the Sikorsky, AceHawk Aerospace is offering a fleet of pre-owned and upgraded S-70 Black Hawks, known as the AceHawk ML-70. Leonardo, which now owns the old Westland Helicopters site at Yeovil in Somerset is strongly pitching its AW189 product. It has unveiled a demonstrator, based on its AW149 helicopter, to spearhead its bid to win the UK's NMH competition.

The AW189 helicopter was painted black at Yeovil and will be used to brief UK Ministry of Defence procurement officials, military personnel, government decision makers and media representatives on the potential of the company's sister AW149 product.

Managing Director of Leonardo Helicopters UK, Nick Whitney, said that the demonstrator helicopter is the same size as a standard AW149, with the same performance. "It will show the helicopter cockpit's open architecture to [demonstrate] what the Ministry of Defence can start with and then modify," said Whitney. "This is not a paper aircraft."

A Leonardo spokesperson said, "The demonstrator [will] highlight

specific characteristics related to the aircraft, including the possibility of choosing between a General Electric or Safran engine. It should be noted that the AW149 was designed as a military helicopter. The AW189 commercial helicopter came later, being developed specifically for the commercial market based on the common platform which originated the AW149."

The speed at which Leonardo is ramping up its campaign to win the NMH competition is a sign of its importance to the company and the long-term future of its Yeovil site, which directly employs 3,000 staff. "It is critical that the Ministry of Defence take this product and become a reference customer," said the Leonardo spokesman. "We will not export successfully without the [UK] operating this aircraft."

ABOVE: The New Medium Helicopter is touted as a replacement for the Griffin HAR2 used by 84 Squadron at RAF Akrotiri in Cyprus. (MOD/CROWN COPYRIGHT)

BELOW: The Puma HC2 is the latest UK variant and is expected to remain in service until the end of the decade. (MOD/CROWN COPYRIGHT)

The Future of UK Airpower

In Demand but Underfunded?

A year ago, the aircraft carrier HMS *Queen Elizabeth* was preparing to sail to the Far East on her maiden operational cruise, with her air group of Royal Navy, Royal Air Force and US Marine Corps Lockheed Martin F-35B Lightning II Jump Jets embarked. Fast forward to the spring of 2022 and the primary focus of British military aviation is reacting to the conflict in Ukraine. In between these two major events, the RAF executed Operation Pitting to evacuate 15,000 civilians fleeing the Taliban from the Afghan capital, Kabul.

Those three major events show just how unpredictable the third decade of the 21st century has become. However, the common thread linking all these events has been the centrality of air power. The F-35B gave HMS *Queen Elizabeth* her punch, backed by her Royal Navy AgustaWestland Merlin HM2 and Wildcat HMA2 helicopters. RAF tactical air transport airport – Boeing

C-17A Globemasters, Airbus A400M Atlas C1s and Lockheed Martin C-130J Hercules C4/C5s – were indispensable to the opening of the air bridge to Hamid Karzai International Airport in Kabul. When it came to helping Ukraine, airpower was again to

the fore. RAF Boeing RC-135 Rivet Joint surveillance aircraft helped to detect the Russian build-up around Ukraine's borders and when it was decided to provide Ukraine with lethal weapons, the RAF's Boeing C-17 Globemasters moved them to

Kyiv within hours of getting the order. When war broke out in February 2022, 99 Squadron's C-17s flew more arms to Poland and the Army Air Corps AgustaWestland Apache AH1s headed to the Baltic States to beef up NATO's defences. Eurofighter Typhoon FGR4s were sent to Romania to protect the skies over the Black Sea.

British airpower was delivered for the British government and people when it mattered. Nowhere was this more decisive than during the Kabul airlift. The eyes of the world were on the Afghan capital and for two dramatic weeks in August 2021 the RAF kept the air bridge open to bring out 15,000 refugees and then recover the 600 British paratroopers who had secured the perimeter around Kabul airport. The British taxpayer got back in spades the RAF's huge investment in state-of-the-art airlifts during those dramatic days.

Looking forward, the RAF, Fleet Air Arm and AAC are being re-equipped to take on the challenges of the coming decades. They are buying new and highly capable aircraft to replace the stalwart flying machines of today. This quest for even better aircraft, sensors and weapons is proving to be very expensive. Back in the late 1970s when the original Panavia Tornado GR1s and F3s were ordered, the RAF paid under £20m for each aircraft. Today there is little change out of £100m for an F-35B.

The RAF ordered some 385 of all versions of the classic Tornado. Over the past two decades it has taken delivery of 160 Typhoons. The initial British order is for 48 F-35Bs and maybe another 20 or so might be bought to cover any attrition. The next generation Tempest combat aircraft has a budget of just over £9bn to design, build and bring it into service. It seems unlikely that this new aircraft will be ordered in the same quantities as the Typhoon and a big chunk of the budget will go on building the unmanned drones that will operate in formation with the Tempest.

As a result, British airpower will have fight and operate in a much smarter way to give the British taxpayer a bigger bang for its pound. There is plenty of talk and investment going into unmanned systems to potentially replace manned aircraft. Work on this is underway and the new Protector will be the first new generation UAV that has been purpose-built for the RAF. More will follow. »

ABOVE: Army Air Corps Apache attack helicopters will have a key role in future land battles. (MOD/CROWN COPYRIGHT)

BELOW: RAF Poseidon MRA1 maritime patrols aircraft allow large areas of sea to be monitored and dominated. (MOD/CROWN COPYRIGHT)

The war in Ukraine and other recent conflicts, including in Nagorno-Karabakh in the South Caucasus, saw the widespread use of cheap but highly effective armed drones. This suggested that maybe one way forward to break the crisis caused by the spiralling cost of modern military hardware would be to accept that it might not always be possible to afford the best technology and kit. Go cheap and get a large number of aircraft that way. However, this would go against 30 years of experience for the British Armed Services, where a fear of failure and losses has driven them to buy ever more capable but expensive equipment. The idea that expensive hi-tech will always win may not necessarily be true. Ukrainian forces, for instance, used swarms of drones to outfox lumbering Russian tank columns and dodge past supersonic Sukhoi Su-35s.

Events of the past year have also shown that high quality aircrew, maintenance personnel and command staff are crucial ingredients in the effective use of airpower. This is one area where the RAF, FAA and AAC have always heavily invested, because they know that skimping on training is a false economy. Finding new ways to cut the cost of training without compromising standards must be a high priority.

In the era of Net Zero to counter the climate crisis, Britain's Armed Forces will be called upon to do their bit to reduce the use of fossil fuels. Non-carbon-based fuels can go some way to help keep legacy aircraft in the air, but in the medium- to long-term electric power will be needed. This will require a whole new generation of military aircraft to replace the

current inventory, possibly as early as the 2040s, which will truly require a revolution in aerospace technology. The civil aerospace sector is already moving in that direction and the world's air forces will have to follow suit if the planet is to be saved.

It is hard to imagine what electric-powered aircraft would mean for air warfare, but the potential is enormous. Air-to-air refuelling aircraft could become obsolete or be transformed into re-charging stations in the sky. Jet noise would be a thing of the past. Fighter pilots would not need to worry about running out of missiles in a dogfight if their aircraft were armed with electric-powered directed energy weapons.